DO YOU KNOW?

How to make a crystal rock garden? How to make soap?
What an electrolyte is?

DO YOU KNOW?

The principle of the phonograph? The reasons for the
behavior of light? The difference between opened,
closed and short circuits? The relationship between
electricity and magnetism?

DO YOU KNOW?

How to bisect an earthworm? How a flower reproduces?
Where bacteria flourish? How to culture a mold?

DO YOU KNOW?

How the slant of the sun's rays affect the temperature?
How to construct a nephoscope? How to make an
anemometer?

DO YOU KNOW?

How to understand the principles of basic algebra?
How to form a perfect square? How to draw a
scalene triangle?

You will enjoy learning all these and many other basic
principles of science with
150 SCIENCE EXPERIMENTS STEP-BY-STEP

BANTAM
SCIENCE
AND
MATHEMATICS

150 Science Experiments Step-By-Step

by Judith Viorst

INTRODUCTION BY WATSON DAVIS
Director, Science Service

Illustrated by Dennis Telesford

BANTAM BOOKS
TORONTO · NEW YORK · LONDON

150 SCIENCE EXPERIMENTS STEP-BY-STEP
Bantam Pathfinder edition published September 1963
2nd printing ..... January 1964
Bantam Science and Mathematics edition published April 1967
4th printing
5th printing
6th printing

Library of Congress Catalog Card Number: 63-15235

Published simultaneously in the United States and Canada

*Bantam Books are published by Bantam Books, Inc., a subsidiary
of Grosset & Dunlap, Inc. Its trade-mark, consisting of the words
"Bantam Books" and the portrayal of a bantam, is registered in the
United States Patent Office and in other countries. Marca Registrada.
Bantam Books, Inc., 271 Madison Avenue, New York, N.Y. 10016.*

PRINTED IN THE UNITED STATES OF AMERICA

INTRODUCTION

Boys and girls who have manipulated wires, heated test tubes, and peered through the microscope know the excitement of experimenting in the sciences. This book is written for them and for all other young people interested in exploring some of nature's basic laws through the experimental process.

There are more than 150 experiments presented here, each with its list of necessary materials and step-by-step instructions. With patience and care, with scrupulous attention to all safety precautions, students should be able to follow these instructions to a successful conclusion, whether it is solving an algebraic puzzle or building a light switch.

The fields covered in this book are chemistry, physics, biology, weather, and numbers. The experiments—designed for grades six to nine or ten—range from easy to challenging. Our goal has been to reach not only those who are firmly committed to a science career, but future poets and presidents, who may be curious about what a cloud is or how plants make their food. We think that one of the best ways to learn about such things is through these experiments, where established scientific truths can be satisfyingly demonstrated—again, and again, and again.

Watson Davis, Director
Science Service

ACKNOWLEDGMENTS

Much of the material in this book is based on classic experiments. In writing the present versions of these experiments, I relied on many people for their vital assistance. I would like to thank, in particular:

From Science Service: Watson Davis, Margit Friedrich, Joseph Kraus, Jane Marye, Marcia Nelson, Dorothy Schriver, Frances Willard, and Ruby Yoshioka.

From the Washington, D. C., school system: Juliette Hughes, Keith Johnson, and Dorothy Smith.

From the National Bureau of Standards: William Dorko, Jack Fath, Karl Goldberg, and Ernest Hughes.

From the United States Weather Bureau: James Beall and John Nyhan.

Friends and patient husband: Jodi Aurelio, Lawrence Kissel, and Milton Viorst.

Judith Viorst

CONTENTS

■ PART 1 CHEMISTRY

■ PART 2 PHYSICS

■ PART 3 BIOLOGY

PART 1
CHEMISTRY

Chemistry is the science that makes sense of flashlight batteries and nylon stockings, mayonnaise and toothpaste. It is the science—as the dictionary says—that describes the composition of substances and explains the various changes which they undergo.

There are good scientific reasons why iron rusts and rain puddles disappear, and why the same three elements can combine to produce substances as different as sugar and vinegar. These reasons have been discovered over the centuries by patient and inquisitive people who were not content to breathe the air without wondering what it was made of.

The following experiments will demonstrate some of these basic laws of chemistry. Many of the chemicals needed for this work can be taken from your kitchen or bathroom shelf; others must be purchased from a pharmacy or a laboratory supply house. Collect bottles of every size and shape, wash them well, and use them for storing all storable chemicals. Be sure to label each container clearly and correctly.

■ SAFETY RULES

You will find that many of the experiments contain words of warning and rules for safety. They are not there because we are particularly nervous, but because we regard them as essential. In addition to individual safety rules given for a particular experiment, we present these general rules that you must follow:

1. Read an experiment through before beginning work on it.

2. Provide adequate ventilation and have an extinguisher handy to put out fires.

3. Inhale vapors cautiously.

4. Keep your face away from materials being heated in a test tube. Hold the tube away from you when heating or shaking.

5. Always wear a rubber apron when you work.

6. Wear goggles when working with heat, with acids or lye, or with any other potentially hazardous materials.

7. Heat materials contained in a flask or test tube clamped to a ring stand by passing the burner back and forth under the container. Don't ever let the flame fix continuously on one point at the bottom of the test tube.

8. Work with small quantities, as directed.

9. Be very careful when working with acids. They can cause serious burns.

10. Keep all containers and equipment clean and keep your working area neat.

11. Never mix chemicals together any which way just to see what happens. You may not be around to find out.

Some of the experiments included in this section are definitely not intended for home use. These are labeled **(with qualified adult supervision only!)**, and must be done at school with a teacher or through a science club with a club sponsor. All experiments requiring a Bunsen burner, or strong acids, or involving serious hazard if performed incorrectly come under this category.

Now that we have completed all our warnings, we want to add a final suggestion—enjoy yourself. Strange as it may seem, being sensible does not make it impossible to have fun.

3

■ MOLECULE MODELS

Purpose

All matter is composed of molecules. Molecules are composed of atoms. The molecules of an element (like iron or oxygen) are made up of identical atoms. The molecules of a compound (like water or sugar), which is a combination of elements, are made up of different types of atoms. The types and the arrangements of atoms in a molecule determine the properties of a compound. For instance, sugar is made up of carbon, hydrogen, and oxygen; so is vinegar. But sugar and vinegar are quite different compounds because a vinegar molecule has 2 carbon atoms, 4 hydrogen atoms, and 2 oxygen atoms; while a sugar molecule has 12 carbon atoms, 22 hydrogen atoms, and 11 oxygen atoms. By making models of the molecules that comprise a few compounds, you can learn some of the ways in which atoms combine.

Apparatus

red clay
white clay
black clay
toothpicks

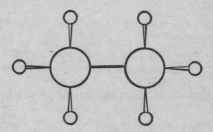

Steps

First prepare the atom molecules.

1. Use the black clay to make three round balls about 1½ inches in diameter.

2. Use the red clay to make three round balls slightly smaller than the black ones.

3. Use the white clay to make 14 tiny white balls.

4. Now fix in your mind what your apparatus represents: The black balls are carbon atoms, the red balls are oxygen atoms, and the white balls are hydrogen atoms. The toothpicks represent chemical bonds, which are the "hands" atoms use to hold on to each other. Each of these atoms has a definite number of bonds—four for carbon, two for oxygen, and one for hydrogen.

Now begin molecule making.

5. Push a toothpick part way into the top of a carbon atom. Push a second toothpick into the bottom, a third into the left side, and a fourth into the right. Your carbon atom now has its four bonds.

6. Attach a hydrogen atom to the end of each carbon bond. You now have the molecule methane, whose chemical designation is CH_4.

7. Prepare a second carbon atom as you did in step 5. Prepare a third, but do not push a toothpick into its left side. Instead, connect the two carbon atoms side by side by pushing the right toothpick of the second carbon atom part way into the left side of the third. (This toothpick actually represents both the right bond of the second carbon atom and the left bond of the third.)

8. Attach hydrogen atoms to the six protruding carbon bonds. You now have the molecule ethane, whose chemical designation is C_2H_6.

9. Set up the following from left to right: a hydrogen atom, an oxygen atom, and another hydrogen atom. Connect them side by side with two bonds, so that your model looks like this: H—O—H. You now have a molecule whose chemical designation is H_2O. We'll let you figure out what the substance is.

10. Set up the following from left to right: a hydrogen atom, an oxygen atom, another oxygen atom, and a second hydrogen atom. Link them side by side with chemical bonds like this: H—O—O—H. This is the hydrogen peroxide molecule, H_2O_2.

Observations

Because hydrogen has only one bond, it can connect at only one point with another atom. Oxygen, with its two bonds, can connect at two points, as in the water molecule and the hydrogen peroxide molecule. Carbon can make a four-way connection, as demonstrated in the methane and ethane molecules.

■ CHEMICAL CHANGE

EXPERIMENT 1

Purpose

Materials change, usually, in one of two ways—physically or chemically. In a physical change the size, shape, or state of a substance may be altered, but the molecules remain the same. In a chemical change, however, new molecules result and new substances are formed. There are four broad categories of chemical change, or reaction: combination, decomposition, simple replacement, and double replacement. Scientists describe such changes by a shorthand method—the chemical equation. In this experiment we will learn the definitions of these four categories of chemical changes and examine the equations that describe them.

Apparatus

pencil and paper

Steps

1. When two or more elements or compounds combine to form a single compound, this chemical reaction is called combination. For instance, the element carbon combines with oxygen gas to form carbon dioxide. The symbol for carbon is C, the symbol for oxygen gas is O_2 (two oxygen atoms), the formula for carbon dioxide is CO_2. The equation for this reaction is $C + O_2 \rightarrow CO_2$. Write the equation for the combination of sulfur, S, and oxygen gas to form sulfur dioxide, SO_2.

2. Decomposition is the breakdown of a compound into simpler substances. Calcium carbonate, $CaCO_3$, decomposes into calcium oxide, CaO, and carbon dioxide. The equation is $CaCO_3 \rightarrow CaO + CO_2$. The compound sulfurous acid, H_2SO_3, decomposes into water and sulfur dioxide. Write the equation for this chemical change.

3. In simple replacement, an atom trades places with another kind of atom in a compound. Thus, when dilute sulfuric acid, H_2SO_4, is poured on zinc, Zn, the zinc replaces

the hydrogen in the acid. The new substances are zinc sulfate and hydrogen gas (two hydrogen atoms). Write the equation.

4. Double replacement occurs when two atoms from two different compounds are interchanged. For instance, hydrochloric acid, HCl, and sodium hydroxide, NaOH, yield water and sodium chloride. Write the equation.

Observations

The four equations are: (1) $S + O_2 \rightarrow SO_2$; (2) $H_2SO_3 \rightarrow H_2O + SO_2$; (3) $Zn + H_2SO_4 \rightarrow ZnSO_4 + H_2$; (4) $HCl + NaOH \rightarrow NaCl + H_2O$. Note that in each case the equation balances, that is, there are the same number of atoms on each side, although they are arranged differently. Often it is necessary to place a number, called a coefficient, in front of symbols and formulas to make an equation balance. For instance, the element magnesium, Mg, can combine with oxygen gas, O_2, to form a new substance, magnesium oxide, MgO. But you can't write $Mg + O_2 \rightarrow MgO$, for this is an unbalanced equation. And you can't write $Mg + O_2 \rightarrow MgO_2$, for MgO_2 is not the symbol for magnesium oxide. The balanced equation for this chemical reaction is $2Mg + O_2 \rightarrow 2MgO$. We have added the coefficient 2 where needed.

EXPERIMENT 2

Purpose
Chemical change by combination will be demonstrated.

Apparatus
stove
pliers or tongs
small piece of pure copper pot-cleaner

Steps

1. Light a burner, grasp the copper with the pliers, and hold it in the flame.

2. After several seconds remove the copper from the flame and examine it.

Observations

The copper combined with oxygen to produce copper oxide, which appears as a black coating on the copper. The symbol for copper is Cu, oxygen gas (made up of two atoms of oxygen) is O_2, copper oxide is CuO. Thus two copper molecules plus the oxygen gas are needed for the reaction. The equation is $2Cu + O_2 \rightarrow 2CuO$.

EXPERIMENT 3

Purpose

Chemical change by decomposition will be demonstrated.

Apparatus

pot
sugar
stove

Steps

1. Put 1 teaspoon sugar in the pot.

2. Put the pot on the stove and heat it.

3. Continue the heat until you have a black mass where the sugar used to be.

Observations

Sugar is composed of three elements—carbon, oxygen, and hydrogen. By heating it you have decomposed it to the compound water, which leaves the sugar as water vapor, and the element carbon, the black mass in the pot. The symbol for sugar is $C_{12}H_{22}O_{11}$. The equation for this reaction is $C_{12}H_{22}O_{11} \rightarrow 12C + 11H_2O$.

EXPERIMENT 4
(With qualified adult supervision only!)

Purpose

Chemical change by simple replacement will be demonstrated.

Apparatus

¼ teaspoon copper sulfate (*Handle carefully—poison!*)
2 ounces water
glass
stirring rod
iron nail

Steps

1. Pour the water into the glass, add the copper sulfate and stir until it dissolves.

2. Dip the nail into the copper-sulfate solution and hold it there for a minute or so.

3. Remove the nail and examine it.

Observations

The iron and the copper have traded places—the iron has gone into solution to form iron sulfate, and the nail is covered with a copper coat. The equation is $Fe + CuSO_4 \rightarrow FeSO_4 + Cu$.

EXPERIMENT 5

(With qualified adult supervision only!)

Purpose

Chemical change by double replacement will be demonstrated.

Apparatus

¼ teaspoon copper sulfate (*Handle carefully—poison!*)
¼ teaspoon barium chloride
4 ounces water
2 glasses
stirring rod

Steps

1. Fill each glass with 2 ounces water.

2. Dissolve the copper sulfate in one glass, the barium chloride in the other.

3. Mix the two solutions together. Set aside for a while and observe what happens.

Observations

A white substance forms and settles to the bottom. A blue solution remains. The white substance is barium sulfate; the blue solution is copper chloride. The sulfate and chloride have exchanged places. The equation for this chemical reaction is $CuSO_4 + BaCl_2 \rightarrow CuCl_2 + BaSO_4$.

SOLUTIONS
AND PRECIPITATES

■ **SOLUTIONS**

Purpose

A mixture is a material made of elements or compounds or both. These substances are not chemically combined, however, and their composition may vary from mixture to mixture. There are non-uniform mixtures, like soil or rocks; and uniform mixtures, like homogeneous solutions. The experiments below will demonstrate some characteristics of solutions.

Apparatus

sugar
water
pot
teaspoon

EXPERIMENT 1

Steps

1. Pour ½ cup of water into the pot.

2. Add 1 spoonful of sugar to the water and stir until it dissolves.

3. Let the mixture stand for a while, then examine it.

4. Continue adding sugar, 1 teaspoon at a time, until no more dissolves, despite stirring and shaking.

Observations

A solution consists of a solvent and a solute, which remain mixed together even after long standing. A solvent is a material capable of dissolving solutes, which, of course, are materials that dissolve. In this experiment we have shown that the sugar-water mixture is a solution. The solvent, water, dissolved the solute sugar and the two substances did not separate on standing. A small amount of solute added to a solvent results in a weak (dilute) solution; a large amount results in a strong (concentrated) solution. When the solute no longer dissolves in the solvent, the solution is saturated.

EXPERIMENT 2

Steps

1. Heat (do not boil) the saturated solution prepared in Experiment 1 and again add sugar until no more dissolves.

2. Pour off any undissolved sugar.

3. Let the solution cool, then examine it.

Observations

Hot water is almost always a better solvent than cold; thus you can dissolve more of the sugar after the water has been heated. This additional solute will reappear, however, when the solution cools.

■ PRECIPITATES

Purpose

Add one solution to another solution and what do you get? A third solution? Not necessarily. You could, instead, produce a solid material—white or bright—from the reaction of two clear liquids. This insoluble solid, which separates out of solution, is called a precipitate. Below are instructions which will enable you to produce three precipitates—in red, white, and blue.

Apparatus

¼ teaspoon dimethyl glyoxime
¼ teaspoon nickel sulfate
½ teaspoon potassium carbonate
¼ teaspoon calcium chloride
⅛ teaspoon ferrous sulfate
¼ teaspoon potassium ferricyanide
ethyl alcohol
water
6 pint bottles
glass stirring rod

EXPERIMENT 1

Steps

1. Fill one pint bottle ¼ full of water; fill another ¼ full of alcohol.

2. Add the dimethyl glyoxime to the alcohol and stir until it dissolves.

3. Add the nickel sulfate to the water and let it stand until it dissolves.

4. Add one solution to the other solution and stir. Let them stand.

EXPERIMENT 2

Steps

1. Fill two bottles ¼ full of water.

2. Add the potassium carbonate to one bottle, the calcium chloride to the other and stir until the solutes are dissolved.

3. Add one solution to the other solution and stir. Let them stand.

EXPERIMENT 3

Steps

1. Fill two bottles ¼ full of water.

2. Add the ferrous sulfate to one bottle and stir.

3. Add the potassium ferricyanide to the other bottle and let it stand until it dissolves.

4. Add one solution to the other solution and stir. Let them stand.

Observations

When the two solutions in Experiment 1 are brought together, the red precipitate nickel dimethyl glyoxime settles out on standing. When the two solutions in Experiment 2 are brought together, the white precipitate calcium carbonate settles out on standing. When the two solutions in Experiment 3 are brought together, the blue precipitate ferrous ferricyanide settles out on standing. Experiment 2 is a typical example of double replacement. When you add potassium carbonate, K_2CO_3, to calcium chloride, $CaCl_2$, the carbonate and chloride change places. The equation for this chemical reaction is $K_2CO_3 + CaCl_2 \rightarrow 2KCl + CaCO_3$.

SUSPENSIONS
AND EMULSIONS

■ SUSPENSIONS

Purpose

What is the difference between a solution and a suspension? The following experiment will give you the answer.

Apparatus

2 glasses
1 jar
1 teaspoon sugar
1 teaspoon mud
water
funnel
filter paper (a disk cut from soft, fine paper such as newspaper)

Steps

1. Fill one glass with water, add the sugar and stir thoroughly.

2. Fill the other glass with water, add the mud and stir thoroughly.

3. Examine the two glasses. The sugar and water are so perfectly mixed that you no longer can distinguish between the two materials. The mud, however, is apparent throughout the water.

4. Fold the filter paper into a cone shape and wet it. Fit it into the funnel and set the funnel in the jar.

5. Pour the sugar-water combination through the filter. On examination you will find that no sugar has been filtered out.

6. Filter the mud-water combination. Flecks of mud will be caught by the paper.

Observations

A suspension is a fluid supporting fine particles which are distributed throughout it. These particles will settle to the bottom of the container. In a solution the solid added to a liquid is not visible (except as coloring) and will not settle. The materials that make up a solution don't separate when filtered; the materials that make up a suspension do.

■ EMULSIONS

Purpose

An emulsion is a combination of liquids that are not inclined to combine. It is the addition of a third ingredient—an emulsifying agent—that forces the uncooperative liquids to get together. Two experiments will demonstrate the characteristics of emulsions.

EXPERIMENT 1

Apparatus
water
water glass
salad oil
soap flakes
cake of soap
salt
teaspoon

Steps

1. Fill the glass halfway with water.

2. Add a teaspoon of oil and stir. Let the oil and water stand—they will quickly separate. Oil and water—as the old saying goes—do not mix.

3. Drop a teaspoonful of soap flakes into the glass and stir. You will find that the oil now spreads throughout the water and does not separate on standing.

4. Empty the glass and wash it out. Fill it again halfway with water.

5. Add salt until you have a saturated solution.

6. Pour some oil on your hands and try to wash them clean, using the salt water and the cake of soap.

Observations

The soap flakes in the first part of the experiment acted as an emulsifying agent, bridging the gap between water and oil and enabling them to mix. In the second part of this experiment, however, soap was unable to act as agent because it was impeded by the salt in the water. Since you can't have an emulsion without an emulsifying agent, the oil and water refused to mix and your hands remained greasy despite the washing.

EXPERIMENT 2

Apparatus

2 eggs
1 cup olive oil
¼ teaspoon salt
2 teaspoons vinegar
mixing bowl
egg beater

Steps

1. Let the eggs stand for a while at room temperature, then break, and separate yolks from whites. Discard the whites (or save them for your mother to use later).

2. Drop the yolks and salt into the mixing bowl and beat with the egg beater.

3. Mix in a teaspoon of vinegar and add ⅓ of the oil, drop by drop, beating steadily.

4. Slowly add the rest of the oil until the mixture thickens.

5. Now blend in the rest of the vinegar and refrigerate the whole concoction.

Observations

You have just prepared homemade mayonnaise, a most edible emulsion. The emulsifying agent in this combination is egg yolk, which joins oil and vinegar together.

CRYSTALS

■ CRYSTALS ON A STRING

Purpose

Crystals are many things—sugar and salt, quartz and dia-
monds. In the following experiments we will work with
kitchen-shelf materials to produce stringfuls of salt and
sugar crystals.

Apparatus

sugar
salt
2 glasses
2 splints of wood
2 strings
water
pot
2 nails

EXPERIMENT 1

Steps

1. Pour a cup of cold water in the pot and add salt until
no more dissolves.

2. Heat (do not boil) the solution and add a final teaspoon
of salt.

3. While waiting for the solution to cool, weight one end
of a piece of string with a nail and tie the other end to the
center of the splint.

16

4. Pour the solution into the glass and place the splint across the top of it so that the string hangs down into the solution.

5. Let the glass stand undisturbed for a few days.

EXPERIMENT 2

Steps

1. Boil a cup of water in the pot, then remove from the heat.

2. Add sugar until no more dissolves.

3. Repeat steps 3 to 5 of Experiment 1.

Observations

As the water evaporates, the salt and the sugar come out of solution in crystal form. The string acts as a nucleus for the crystals, which grow up and around it. The crystals formed by the sugar are known as rock candy and can be eaten.

■ CRYSTALS ON A GLASS

Purpose

Grow crystals on the outside of a plain tumbler or vase, and you will have frosted glass.

Apparatus

Epsom salts (magnesium sulfate)
½ cup water
liquid glue
pot
small paint brush
tumbler or vase

Steps

1. Fill the pot with the water and boil. Turn off the heat.

2. Add Epsom salts until no more dissolves.

3. Add a few drops of liquid glue and stir.

4. Dip the brush into the pot and apply the liquid to the tumbler or vase.

Observations

In a short while the liquid evaporates and frosty crystals form on the glass.

■ CRYSTALS IN A GARDEN

Purpose

When a solution of salt dissolved in water is left undisturbed, the water evaporates and the salt remains as beautiful crystals. In the following experiment we will apply this principle to growing a colorful crystal garden at home.

Apparatus

several small lumps of coal or coke
6 tablespoons salt
6 tablespoons water
1½ tablespoons ammonia water
12 drops of Mercurochrome
12 drops of bluing
large glass bowl or dish

Steps

1. Mix the salt, water, and ammonia water together.

2. Place the coal in the bowl and pour the liquid over it.

3. Drop the bluing on some pieces of the coal, the Mercurochrome on others.

4. Let the bowl stand undisturbed for several days.

Observations

Crystals will cling to the lumps of coal and cover them, growing in attractive patterns. The crystals will be the flowers of your garden, colored in part by the bluing and Mercurochrome, white where no coloring fell.

■ **ACIDS AND ALKALIS**

Purpose

Scientists have developed various tests for identifying unknown materials. Sometimes a test provides very precise identification; sometimes it merely indicates the general category into which Material X falls. Litmus paper is a most useful chemical private eye, for it indicates the presence of acids or alkalis (also called bases) and indicates, too, if the tested material is neutral (neither acid nor alkali). Below are some chemical tests using litmus paper.

Apparatus

6 strips of red litmus paper
6 strips of blue litmus paper
lemon juice
vinegar
ammonia water
milk of magnesia
milk
water
6 cups (or equivalent containers)
tablespoon

EXPERIMENT 1

Steps

1. Put 2 tablespoons of lemon juice in one cup, 2 tablespoons of vinegar in another. (Always wash the tablespoon before measuring out a new material.)

2. Take a small taste of each. Both will have the sour taste characteristic of acids.

3. Dip one piece of red litmus into the vinegar, another into the lemon juice. Do the same with two pieces of blue litmus.

Observations

Acids turn blue litmus paper red. The red litmus paper will remain red.

EXPERIMENT 2

Steps

1. Put 2 tablespoons of ammonia water in one cup, 2 table-spoons of milk of magnesia in another.

2. Do not taste or handle. Alkalis are bitter tasting, and ammonia water is poisonous.

3. Dip one piece of red litmus into the ammonia water, another into the milk of magnesia. Do the same with two pieces of blue litmus.

Observations

Alkalis (bases) turn red litmus paper blue. The blue litmus paper will not change color.

EXPERIMENT 3

Steps

1. Put 2 tablespoons of water in one cup, 2 tablespoons of milk in another. (Be sure that the milk is fresh.)

2. We will assume you have tasted both of these. If you recall, they are neither bitter nor sour.

3. Dip one piece of red litmus into the water, another into the milk. Do the same with two pieces of blue litmus.

Observations

A material which contains neither an acid nor a base is neutral. Materials are neutralized when an acid and an alkali are combined so that neither remains after the chemical change is complete. Neutrals do not affect litmus paper —the blue is still blue and the red is still red.

■ FLAME TESTS

(With qualified adult supervision only!)

Purpose

A chemical is added to a plain blue flame, and suddenly it burns with a yellow, or green, or crimson, or violet glow. Elements display characteristic colors when heated, as the following flame tests will show.

Apparatus

Bunsen burner
table salt
baking soda
cupric chloride crystals, just a few
potassium carbonate solution (½ teaspoon potassium carbonate to 1 glass of water)
pliers or tongs
piece of blue glass
nichrome wire, a few inches long

Steps

1. Light the burner and adjust to a blue flame.

2. Drop a little salt into the flame. Add a pinch of baking soda. What is the color of the flame now?

3. Use the tongs to grasp a cupric chloride crystal and hold it in the flame. What is the color?

4. Dip an end of the nichrome wire into the potassium carbonate solution. Grasp the wire with the tongs and hold the wetted end in the flame. What is the color?

Observations

The element sodium, present in both the table salt and the baking soda, gives a bright yellow color. Copper, present in the cupric chloride crystal, colors the flame green. Potassium colors it violet—if you get yellow, observe the flame through the blue glass to block out the impurities. Those who want to pursue flame tests further can try for a brilliant red strontium flame, an orange-red flame from calcium and a yellow-green flame from barium.

■ OXYGEN

(With qualified adult supervision only!)

Purpose

Oxygen, as everyone knows, is vitally necessary to life. On earth we breathe it from the air; in space, astronauts carry along a supply of this gas in order to survive where no oxygen exists. Oxygen does not burn, but it supports combustion. That is why space rockets as well as spacemen must be equipped with oxygen in order to function beyond the earth. Directions for generating oxygen and demonstrating its ability to support combustion are given below.

Apparatus

5 grams potassium chlorate
2 grams manganese dioxide
water
spatula
piece of clean paper
dry test tube
one-hole rubber stopper
short length glass tubing
longer length rubber tubing
baking pan or trough
2 small jars
2 glass plates
piece of charcoal
long splinter of wood
Bunsen burner
ring stand and clamp
tongs or pliers
towel

Steps

First collect two jars of oxygen.

1. With the spatula thoroughly mix the potassium chlorate and the manganese dioxide on the paper. Do not grind or crush.

2. Transfer the mixture to the test tube and attach the stopper.

3. Insert the glass tubing through the stopper hole, attach the rubber tubing to the glass. Whenever you insert glass tubing through a stopper, wet the tubing to avoid breaking, and protect your hand by wrapping a towel around it.

4. Clamp the test tube to the ring stand.

5. Fill the pan halfway with water. Invert a jar of water into the pan. Extend the rubber tubing from the test tube into the mouth of the jar. Lean the jar against a corner of the pan to steady it.

6. Heat the test tube *very gently, slowly, and evenly* by moving the burner back and forth under it. As the oxygen is liberated from the potassium chlorate, it will displace the water from the jar. Let the oxygen bubble through the water at an even rate. If the bubbles are too rapid, apply less heat; if too slow, apply more heat.

7. When the jar is filled with oxygen (when all the water in the jar has been displaced), take the rubber tubing out of the pan immediately. (Otherwise the water in the pan will be sucked back into the hot test tube.) Slip a wet glass plate under the mouth of the jar and set it right side up on a table. Keep the covering on the jar till ready for use.

8. Fill the other jar in the same way.

Now try these experiments with the oxygen:

9. Ignite the splinter of wood, then blow it out. When only a spark remains, immerse it in one of the jars of oxygen.

10. Heat a piece of charcoal until it glows, then use the tongs to insert it into the other jar of oxygen.

Observations

The wood splinter burns anew in the bottle of oxygen, and the glowing charcoal flares brightly. In both cases the experiment shows that oxygen supports combustion. The equation for obtaining oxygen is $2KClO_3 \xrightarrow{MnO_2} 2KCl + 3O_2$. The manganese dioxide, whose formula is placed over the arrow, merely acts as a catalyst in this reaction. It forces the potassium chlorate, $KClO_3$, to release its oxygen faster, while remaining itself unchanged.

■ CARBON DIOXIDE

Purpose

Carbon dioxide, CO_2, turns up in a variety of places. It is used in fire extinguishers to battle flames, and in flavored water to produce *carbon*ated soda. In its solid form it is dry ice—so called because it goes from a solid to a gas state without going through the liquid state at all. Some of the properties of CO_2 are demonstrated in the experiments below, where you will also learn how to generate this gas from two simple around-the-house materials.

Apparatus

4 teaspoons baking soda
8 teaspoons vinegar
quart jar
pliers or tongs
wood splint
candle
small plate
6 tablespoons limewater
2 small jars

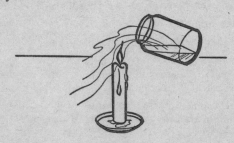

EXPERIMENT 1

Steps

1. Place ½ the baking soda in the quart jar and pour ½ the vinegar over it. A great fizzing and foaming will immediately occur as the acid in the vinegar reacts with the soda to form CO_2. Your quart jar now contains carbon dioxide gas.

2. Use the pliers or tongs to lower a lighted splint into the mouth of the jar. The flame will go out.

3. Wash out the quart jar and use the rest of the soda and vinegar to prepare more CO_2.

4. Light the candle and let some of the heated wax drip on the plate. Anchor the candle to the plate by pressing the bottom of it against the hot wax. Now that the candle is safely fastened, tip the quart jar over the candle flame and let the gas (not the liquid) flow over it. (Save some gas for the next experiment.) The flame will go out.

Observations

Fire will not burn in carbon dioxide because this gas neither burns nor supports combustion. It is possible to pour carbon dioxide out of the jar—just as you would pour a liquid—because this gas is heavier than air.

EXPERIMENT 2

Steps

1. Divide the limewater equally between the two small jars. Cap and shake. The limewater will remain clear, or cloud very slightly.

2. Pour the remaining CO_2 from your quart jar into one of the jars. Cap and shake. The limewater will become cloudy.

3. Breathe into the other jar. Cap and shake. The limewater will become cloudy.

Observations

When CO_2 is added to limewater, $Ca(OH)_2$, the resulting reaction forms calcium carbonate, $CaCO_3$, and water. Since no other gas affects limewater in this way, the change from clear to cloudy indicates the presence of carbon dioxide. The clouding that may occur in step 1 is due to the carbon dioxide in the air. The reason why we can turn limewater cloudy with our breath is, of course, because we exhale

CO_2. The equation for the reaction is $Ca(OH)_2 + CO_2 \rightarrow CaCO_3 + H_2O$.

■ NITROGEN

(With qualified adult supervision only!)

Purpose

Nitrogen does not support combustion. It does not readily combine with other elements. It isn't lively like oxygen, explosive like hydrogen, or heavy like carbon dioxide. Yet without the presence of this gas, the processes of rusting and decay would be greatly hastened, and life itself would probably be much shorter. Although nitrogen does not easily lend itself to dramatic experimentation, you can generate it and collect it over water. Directions follow.

Apparatus

5 grams sodium nitrite
4 grams ammonium chloride
water
glass stirring rod
large flask
two-hole stopper to fit flask
thistle tube
short length of glass tubing
longer length of rubber tubing
baking pan or trough
small jar
glass plate
Bunsen burner
ring stand and clamp
long splinter of wood

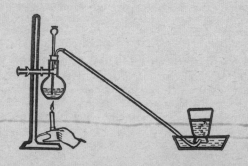

Steps

1. Place the sodium nitrite and ammonium chloride in the flask and mix with the glass rod. Attach the stopper to the flask.

2. Fit the thistle tube into one of the stopper's holes. Fit the glass tubing into the other hole, then attach the rubber tubing to the glass.

3. Fill the pan part way with water. Fill the jar with water and invert it into the pan.

4. Clamp the flask to the stand. Extend the unattached end of the rubber tubing into the pan.

5. Pour about 30 cc of cold water into the thistle tube and heat the flask gently by moving the burner back and forth under it. Be sure the thistle tube is below the surface of the water. The released nitrogen will be delivered through the tubing and will bubble through the water in the pan.

6. When the bubbles begin to form rapidly, remove the heat from the flask and slip the rubber tubing under the mouth of the jar. The nitrogen will displace the water in the jar. If the bubbles form too violently, pour more water through the thistle tube. If the action is too slow, very gently apply heat to the flask once more.

7. When the water in the jar is completely displaced, slip the glass plate under the jar and remove from the pan. Stand the jar right side up, keeping it covered with the plate.

8. Light the splint and place it in the mouth of the jar. The flame will go out.

Observations

Like CO_2, nitrogen will not support combustion. Unlike this gas, however, nitrogen is lighter than air and will rise from the jar if not held inside by the plate. In this reaction, sodium nitrite, $NaNO_2$, and ammonium chloride, NH_4Cl, yielded sodium chloride, $NaCl$, and water, as well as nitrogen gas. The equation is $NaNO_2 + NH_4Cl \rightarrow NaCl + N_2 + 2H_2O$.

■ **OXIDATION**

Purpose

Organic chemistry studies carbon and its compounds. Inorganic chemistry studies all other elements and compounds. The combination of a substance with oxygen, called oxidation, can be either an organic or inorganic chemical reaction, depending on the composition of the substance. The rusting of iron is inorganic oxidation. It will be demonstrated below.

Apparatus

tall drinking glass
½ ball of steel wool (composed of iron)
soup bowl
water
paper towels

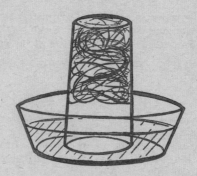

Steps

1. Run water over the steel wool until it is thoroughly soaked, then squeeze the water from it.

2. Pull out the steel wool so that it is fluffy instead of firmly packed, then put it in the glass. It should occupy about half the space.

3. Invert the glass, making sure that the steel wool does not slip from position—the top half of the inverted glass—and stand it in the bowl.

4. Fill the bowl halfway with water. No water should enter the glass at this point.

5. Let the glass stand undisturbed in the bowl for 48 hours. How much of the glass is filled with water now?

6. Remove the steel wool and dry it off with the paper towels. What comes off on the towels?

Observations

Water fills 20% of the glass, replacing the oxygen that was used up when it united with the iron in the steel wool. (Oxygen, as you recall, makes up 20% of the air.) When iron and oxygen combine, they form iron oxide, the rust that you wiped from the steel wool. The equation for this reaction is $4Fe + 3O_2 \rightarrow 2Fe_2O_3$.

■ REDUCTION

(With qualified adult supervision only!)

Purpose

The removal of oxygen from a compound is one type of reduction. The substance that removes the oxygen is called a reducing agent. The following experiment will demonstrate reduction, using carbon—charcoal—as the reducing agent.

Apparatus

charcoal block
yellow lead oxide, very small amount
Bunsen burner
blowpipe
small spatula
tongs
goggles

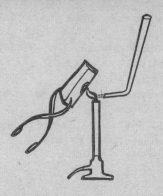

Steps

1. Use the spatula to scrape out a small cavity in the charcoal block.

2. Place the lead oxide in the cavity. Hold the block with the tongs for the rest of this experiment, to protect your fingers from the heat.

3. Direct the flame of the burner onto the lead oxide by blowing on the flame through the blowpipe. Hold the pipe slightly away from the flame and blow gently and steadily to obtain a yellow flame. It might take a little practice to use the blowpipe correctly. (Be sure to wear your goggles.)

4. Continue blowing until globules of lead form.

Observations

The charcoal combines with the oxygen in the lead oxide, leaving the free metal. The equation for this reaction is $2PbO + C \rightarrow 2Pb + CO_2$.

■ HYDROLYSIS

(With qualified adult supervision only!)

Purpose

Hydrolysis is decomposition by water. Included in this term is saponification—the making of soap. In saponification a fat is treated with water plus a hydrolyzing agent to produce soap plus glycerin. The following experiment will demonstrate this organic reaction, using the alkali sodium hydroxide as the hydrolyzing agent.

Apparatus

15 grams of lard
4 grams of sodium hydroxide (lye) (*Handle with care—can cause burns!*)
15 cc water
small casserole
jar
glass stirring rod
Bunsen burner
ring stand and ring clamp
square of asbestos wire gauze

Steps

1. Attach the ring clamp to the ring stand and set the asbestos on the clamp.

2. Place the lard in the casserole and set the casserole on the clamp.

3. Pour the water into the jar and dissolve the sodium hydroxide. (*Caution: A great amount of heat will develop in the jar. Caution: Do not splash the solution on yourself.*) Don't worry if some of the sodium hydroxide pellets stick to the bottom of the jar. They will eventually dissolve.

4. Use your Bunsen burner to apply gentle heat to the lard.

5. When the lard is melted, add the sodium hydroxide solution to it, slowly and carefully, stirring constantly.

6. Continue the heat for 5 to 10 minutes, still stirring constantly, until the material hardens.

7. Let the casserole cool, then wash off the material with water to get rid of any excess sodium hydroxide on the outside.

Observations

The hydrolysis of the fat (the lard) with the alkali (the sodium hydroxide) and water is now complete. You have just manufactured crude soap. (*Caution: Do not use it on your skin. It can cause irritation and possibly burn.*) In large-scale manufacture of soap the fat used is stearin. The equation for the reaction is

$$C_3H_5(C_{17}H_{35}COO)_3 + 3NaOH \rightarrow$$

STEARIN   ALKALI

$$3C_{17}H_{35}COONa + C_3H_5(OH)_3.$$

SOAP   GLYCERIN

■ ACETYLATION

(With qualified adult supervision only!)

Purpose

Acetylation is the process of replacing the hydrogen atoms of certain organic compounds with the acetyl group. This reaction is used to produce acetylsalicylic acid—the scientific name of a well-known drugstore item. The following experiment will demonstrate how it is done.

Apparatus

2 cc acetic acid (*Do not touch—can cause burns!*)
2 cc acetic anhydride
2 grams salicylic acid
water
beaker
small flask
ring stand and clamp
Bunsen burner
glass stirring rod
pot holder

Steps

1. Pour the acetic acid and acetic anhydride into the flask and stir.

2. Add the salicylic acid.

3. Clamp the flask to the ring stand and boil gently for 10 minutes, moving the burner back and forth beneath the flask.

4. Wait a few minutes, then fill the beaker ¾ full of cold water, grasp the flask with the pot holder and pour the hot solution into the beaker. Crude aspirin (*Not for consumption!*) will separate out.

Observations

In this organic reaction the hydrogen of salicylic acid, $C_6H_4(OH)COOH$, is replaced by the acetyl group, CH_3CO, through acetylation, to produce the aspirin,

$$C_6H_4(OCOCH_3)COOH.$$

■ **ELECTROPLATING**

(With qualified adult supervision only!)

Purpose

Electricity flowing through a solution can produce chemical changes. It can, for instance, coat a piece of iron with a layer of chrome by taking the chromium out of solution and depositing it on the iron. This method of coating a material with a layer of metal is called electroplating. The following experiment will demonstrate the process, using an old piece of silverware as the object to be plated, and copper as the metal to be deposited.

Apparatus

1 teaspoon copper-sulfate crystals (*Handle carefully—poison!*)
6 ounces of water
drinking glass
2 pieces insulated copper bell wire, each at least 12 inches long
strip of pure copper, about 2 inches long and ½ inch wide
No. 6 dry cell with screw terminals
old silver-plated spoon (Be sure it is expendable.)
knife
steel wool

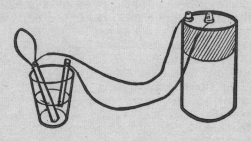

Steps

1. Mix the copper sulfate and the water in the glass.

2. Scrape off 2 inches of coating on both ends of both pieces of wire with the knife.

3. Thoroughly clean the spoon with the steel wool.

4. Tie one of the bare ends of wire to the spoon. Tie the other end to the negative terminal of the dry cell. (This terminal is located near the edge.)

5. Tie one end of the second wire to the strip of copper. Tie the other end to the positive terminal of the dry cell. (This terminal is located at the center.)

6. Insert the copper strip and the spoon handle into the solution to complete the circuit. Don't let them touch each other.

Observations

In a short time the spoon handle will become coated with copper metal. Copper sulfate is an electrolyte, a chemical that conducts electricity when dissolved in water. The electric current charges the spoon negatively and the spoon then attracts the copper in solution, which is positively charged. (Be sure that the spoon, or any object that is to be coated, is always attached to the negative terminal, or else the experiment won't work.)

■ ELECTROCHEMICAL CELLS

(With qualified adult supervision only!)

Purpose

Both wet and dry cells are made up of materials arranged to produce an electric current by chemical reaction. In the following experiment you will make a wet cell and demonstrate that it generates electricity.

Apparatus

1 copper strip, 1 inch wide by 5 inches long
1 zinc strip, 1 inch wide by 5 inches long
12 inches of insulated copper bell wire
100 cc dilute sulfuric acid (*Do not touch—can cause burns!*)
beaker
knife

Steps

1. Pour the acid carefully into the beaker.

2. Use the knife to bare the wire 4 inches at one end, 1 inch at the other.

3. Wrap the 4-inch bared end of wire around the top of the copper strip and stand the strip—by its unwired end—in the beaker.

4. Stand the zinc in the beaker, making sure that it does not touch the copper.

5. Examine the behavior of the metal strips in the jar. Does the copper react to the acid? Does the zinc?

6. Touch the 1-inch bared end of wire to the top of the zinc strip and hold it there for a few minutes. How does the copper strip behave now?

Observations

When the zinc is immersed in the acid, bubbles are given off from the strip. The copper strip, however, does not react with the acid, and no bubbles appear around it. When you connect the two metals in an electric current, electrons flow from zinc (the more active metal) to copper. When these electrons come into contact with the acid ions around the copper strip, bubbles of hydrogen gas are given off at the surface of this strip. Thus the presence of bubbles around the copper shows that the cell is generating electricity.

PART 2
PHYSICS

A disk that preserves and reproduces music, a box that captures and records an image, a switch that throws a machine into motion—each is the product of the fundamental science of physics. Physics is the study of the nature and behavior of material things, which are any things that have weight or occupy space. Included in this study are heat and light, electricity and magnetism, radiation, and a variety of forces investigated under the subdivision of physics known as mechanics.

In this section you will experiment with vibration and reflection and conduction, with gravity and inertia. With easy-to-assemble equipment, you will build your own light switch, electromagnet and kaleidoscope, as well as musical instruments and simple machines. By the time you complete the following experiments, you should be acquainted with some of the basic laws of our physical universe.

■ TRAVELING SOUNDS

Purpose

When an object vibrates, it moves back and forth, compressing air molecules (condensation), then letting them expand (rarefaction), again and again until the vibrations cease. This activity sets up waves, which travel through the air and reach our ears as sounds. Liquids also carry sounds, as you can easily demonstrate the next time you go for a swim. (Submerge your head, and have a friend clonk two stones together under water at some distance from you.) Sounds are carried by solids, too, as the following experiment will show.

Apparatus

2 used tin cans, opened at one end, closed at the other
hammer and nail
2 buttons
sturdy piece of thread, 9 feet long

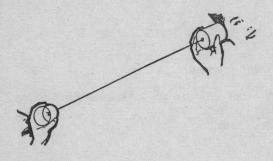

Steps

1. Make a hole in the bottom center of each can by hammering the nail through it.

2. Connect the cans with the thread, stretched from bottom to bottom. To keep the thread from slipping out of the holes, tie each end to a button placed on the inside of the cans.

3. Take hold of one can and give the other to a friend. Move apart until the thread is taut.

4. Ask your friend to talk into the open end of his can while you listen through the open end of yours. You should be able to hear him, even when he speaks softly.

Observations

Sound waves travel through solids—in this case through the thread. The bottom of the can acts as a diaphragm, which vibrates when your friend speaks.

■ MUSICAL SOUNDS

Purpose

When the vibrations of an object are irregular, the result is discord, or noise. Regular vibrations, however, can produce a sound of music. Musical sounds may come from the vibration of strings, of columns of air or of solid objects. Below are instructions for making simple string, wind, and percussion instruments.

Apparatus

cigar box
string, about 5 times the length of the box
scissors
8 screw eyes
5 soda bottles, same size
water
½-pint cardboard container (cylinder-shape) with top
pencil
transparent tape
handful of pebbles

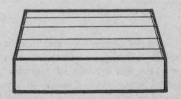

EXPERIMENT 1

Steps

1. Remove the top of the cigar box.

2. Screw in four screw eyes along one of the shorter top edges of the box. The outer eyes should be about ½ inch in from the ends.

3. Repeat step 2 along the opposite top edge of the box.

4. Cut the string into four equal pieces and connect each piece from screw eye to opposite screw eye. Twist the eyes until the strings are taut.

5. Pluck the strings with your fingers.

6. Vary the tension of the strings by tightening and loosening the screw eyes. See if you can produce four distinctly different musical sounds.

Observations

The cigar box makes music when your fingers vibrate the strings. The tighter the string and the shorter it is, the faster the vibrations and the higher the pitch. (Thin strings have a higher pitch than thick strings. See if you can devise an experiment to demonstrate.)

EXPERIMENT 2

Steps

1. Line up the soda bottles, side by side, on a table.

2. Add a different amount of water to each bottle.

3. Blow across the top of each bottle in turn, and listen to the sounds you produce. Which bottle has the lowest pitch? Which has the highest?

Observations

This soda-bottle wind instrument produces music when your breath vibrates the air columns in the bottles. The variations in pitch depend on the amount of water in the bottles: the more water, the shorter the column of air, the faster the vibrations, the higher the pitch. Perhaps you can play a little tune on your bottles.

EXPERIMENT 3

Steps

1. Remove the top of the cardboard container and make a small hole in the center.

2. Insert the pencil about an inch or two into the hole, then wrap transparent tape around the inserted end until there is enough thickness to prevent the pencil from slipping out. Also wrap tape around the outside of the pencil, where it meets the hole, to prevent it from slipping in.

3. Drop the pebbles into the container, put back the top and tape it in place.

4. Use the pencil as a handle to shake your rattle.

Observations

This simple percussion instrument has no variations in pitch. You can obtain a variety of sounds from rattles, however, by making them of different materials—metal, for example, with rice for filler.

■ RECORDING SOUNDS

Purpose

The invention of the phonograph has made it possible to preserve and reproduce sound waves. The waves are traced onto a disk by a vibrating needle; later, a second needle retraces these recorded patterns, and the original sounds are heard once again. Below is a little experiment to introduce you to the workings of the phonograph.

Apparatus

phonograph
old 78 rpm record
straight pin
sheet of paper

Steps

1. Turn on the phonograph and hold the straight pin over the record, touching it gently. Do you hear sounds?

2. Roll the paper into a megaphone and pierce the tapered end with the pin. Now repeat step 1. How is the sound affected?

Observations

You hear a faint sound from the record as you "play" the phonograph with the pin. When the pin causes the megaphone to vibrate, the sounds are amplified.

HEAT

■ HEAT EXPANSION

Purpose

According to current theory, heat is energy resulting from molecular activity. When something is heated, its molecules move faster and push farther and farther apart. In this way heating causes solids, liquids, and gases to expand. A steel ball just barely able to pass through a steel ring no longer passes through when heated. Heat makes the mercury in a thermometer rise. The following experiment will demonstrate how heat causes air to expand.

Apparatus

saucepan
soda bottle
balloon (uninflated)
water
stove

Steps

1. Fit the mouth of the balloon snugly over the mouth of the bottle.

2. Stand the bottle in the saucepan, fill the pan with 1 inch of water and heat on the stove. What happens to the balloon?

Observations

The air inside the bottle expands when heated, moves into the balloon and inflates it.

■ CONDUCTION OF HEAT

Purpose

Heat can be transferred by radiation, convection, or conduction. Radiation is responsible for the warmth you feel from the sun: the sun's heat is converted to radiant energy, travels by wave motion through airless space and through the atmosphere, and is absorbed by your body. In convection heating, the heavier cool air falls, pushing up the lighter hot air in a continuous current. When heat is conducted, it moves along an object, speeding up the motion of molecules all along the way. For a demonstration of heat conduction, follow the directions below.

Apparatus

4 paper clips
thread
candle in candlestick
plate
steel knitting needle, about 14 inches long
pot holder

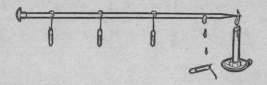

Steps

1. Tie a small piece of thread to each clip.

2. Light the candle and let some wax drip onto the plate.

3. Use the hot wax drippings to hang the clips, by their threads, from the knitting needle. The clips should be an equal distance from each other and about 1½ inches in from the ends.

4. Grasp the needle with the pot holder, and hold the pointed end in the candle flame. Observe what happens to the clips.

Observations

Heat is conducted from one end of the needle to the other—thus the clip nearest the flame falls off first when the heat melts the wax. As the heat continues on its way, the other clips fall off in turn.

■ ABSORPTION, REFLECTION, RADIATION

Purpose

A dark, dull surface heats and cools rapidly; a shiny metal or white-painted surface heats and cools slowly. The reason? The dark surface absorbs heat when cool, radiates it outward when warmed. The light surface is a poor absorber and radiator. Instead, it reflects most of the light waves and bounces them back to their source. Two experiments will demonstrate absorption, reflection, and radiation.

Apparatus

2 glass plates, same size
2 ice cubes, same size
2 pieces of cloth, same material and size—one black, one white
flat black paint
paint brush
light bulb
shiny tin can, larger than the bulb

EXPERIMENT 1

Steps

1. Place an ice cube on each plate.

2. Cover one with the black cloth, the other with the white cloth.

3. Set the plates in the sun. Which ice cube melts faster?

Observations

The cube covered with the black cloth melts first because the dark surface absorbs heat, while the white surface reflects it.

EXPERIMENT 2

Steps

1. Paint half the can (vertically) with the black paint, inside and out. Let the other half remain shiny.

2. When the paint dries, turn on the bulb and let it hang into the can.

3. Place both hands on the outside of the can, one on the shiny section, the other on the black section. Which side is warmer?

Observations

The black surface is warmer than the shiny surface because it radiates more heat.

LIGHT

■ HOW LIGHT TRAVELS

Purpose

Most scientists today go along with the theory that light consists of bundles of energy called photons, which travel by means of waves. The precise nature of light can only be discussed theoretically, but certain aspects of its behavior can be demonstrated. See the experiments below.

Apparatus

4 cardboard cards, 4 inches square
4 small wooden blocks
8 thumbtacks
scissors
ruler
matches
short thick candle, about 2 inches high, on a plate
drinking glass
water
pencil

EXPERIMENT 1

Steps

1. Measure, cut out, and discard a 1-inch square from the center of each card. Be accurate—the cutouts must occur in the identical place on each card.

2. Tack the bottoms of the cards to the blocks so that the cards stand upright.

3. Line up the cards behind each other, 12 inches apart.

4. Stand the candle directly behind the hole in the last card and light it.

5. Adjust the candle and the cards so that they are in a perfectly straight line, and look through the first hole. You will be able to see the candlelight at the other end.

6. Move one of the cards slightly to the left or right so that the holes are not aligned, and look through the first hole again. The candlelight is no longer visible.

Observations

Light rays travel in a straight line.

EXPERIMENT 2

Steps

1. Fill the glass halfway with water and stand the pencil in it so that it is only partly immersed.

2. Observe the pencil from various positions. You will find that in most positions it appears to be bent.

Observations

It is the light reflected from the pencil, of course, not the pencil itself, that actually bends. This bending is called refraction. Refraction occurs when light waves pass from one medium to another of different density, and as a result, move either faster or slower. A light wave moves more slowly in the water than it does in the air. The part of the wave that strikes the water first slows down, while the part still traveling in the air continues at its regular speed. This causes the wave to change direction—to bend.

■ MIRRORS AND LIGHT

Purpose

When you look at yourself in a mirror, you see your reflection. It is visible because the light from your body is reflected off the surface of the mirror and back into your eyes. A reflection obeys certain rules. It appears to be as far behind the mirror as the object is in front of it; it appears as large as the object; it is erect; it is reversed. Other characteristics of light and mirrors may be observed in the following experiments.

Apparatus

3 pocket mirrors, about 2 inches by 3 inches
sheet of white paper
ruler
protractor
pencil
dime
rubber band
piece of cardboard
colored papers (5 or 6 different colors)
scissors

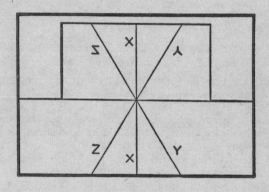

EXPERIMENT 1

Steps

1. Draw a straight line on the sheet of white paper. Call this line X.

2. Draw another straight line at any angle to X. Call the line Y.

3. Stand a mirror at the point where the angle is formed and adjust it until the reflected X is in a straight line with the actual X.

4. Look at Y in the mirror and place the ruler on the paper so that it is lined up with the reflected Y. Draw this line on the paper from the point where it meets the mirror. Call it Z.

5. With the protractor, measure the angle formed by X and Z, and the angle formed by X and Y. Are they the same?

Observations

Line Y represents a ray of light striking the mirror. Line Z represents a ray of light leaving the mirror. The angle formed by the perpendicular X and Y is called the angle of incidence. The angle formed by X and Z is called the angle of reflection. According to the Law of Reflection, the angle of incidence equals the angle of reflection.

EXPERIMENT 2

Steps

1. Stand two mirrors on edge, long sides horizontal, and form a 90° angle. The reflecting surfaces should face each other.

2. Place the dime in front of and in between the two mirrors. How many dimes do you see? Adjust the mirror angle until you can see 70 cents' worth of dimes.

Observations

As you narrow the angle, more images appear because the light from the coin is reflected back and forth between the mirrors a greater number of times.

EXPERIMENT 3

Steps

1. Stand the three mirrors on edge, long sides vertical, and form a triangle, reflecting sides facing inward. Use the rubber band to hold the mirrors in place.

2. Cut the colored papers into tiny pieces and place them on the cardboard.

3. Close one eye and look down at the papers through your triangle of mirrors.

Observations

You will see a beautiful geometric pattern through the mirrors, which serve as a simple kaleidoscope. Shake the cardboard to rearrange the pieces, and another pattern will form. In the kaleidoscope, light from the bits of paper is reflected from each mirror, and each mirror reflects the reflections of the other two mirrors as well.

■ PHOTOGRAPHY AND LIGHT

Purpose

A camera captures and records images with a convex lens and film. The following experiments will show how light can cause a chemical change in sensitized paper (such as film) and how a lens can focus light to produce an image.

Apparatus

¼ ounce silver nitrate (*Caution: Causes burns—poisonous!*)
¼ ounce table salt
1 pint water
2 soup bowls
3 pieces of paper, 4 inches square
large piece of cardboard
button
key
ring (dime-store variety)
stirring rod
tweezers
fluorescent lamp
reading glass
large piece of heavy white paper
pencil and paper

EXPERIMENT 1

Steps

1. Mix the silver nitrate and ½ pint of the water in one of the bowls. (*Caution: The solution stains.*)

2. Mix the salt and the remaining ½ pint of water in the other bowl.

3. Soak the three pieces of paper in the silver nitrate solution. (Use the tweezers to handle them.)

4. Remove the paper to the salt solution and leave the pieces there until they are well coated with a white film. This is a precipitate of sodium chloride.

5. Place the pieces of paper on the cardboard and immediately put the button on one piece, the key on another, the ring on the third.

6. Lay the cardboard under the fluorescent lamp for 20 minutes, then remove the objects from the treated papers. What has happened?

Observations

Light decomposes the silver chloride and the paper darkens— except where it is covered. Thus you have a picture of a button, a key and a ring. Camera film, which is also sensitive to light, behaves in a similar way when the image of an object falls upon it.

EXPERIMENT 2

Steps

1. Stand in front of a sunlit window and select some nearby object, such as a tree or a car.

2. Hold the heavy white paper in one hand. Hold the reading glass in the other, between the paper and the window.

3. Move the glass back and forth until it forms a clear but upside-down image of the object on the paper.

Observations

The reading glass behaves like a camera lens, bending the light rays coming from the object and bringing them to a focus on the paper. To learn why the image is inverted, do the next experiment.

EXPERIMENT 3

Steps

1. Draw a vertical line on the left side of the paper. Label it *object*. Label the top X, the bottom Y.

2. Draw a dot a few inches to the right of the line and halfway between X and Y. Label it *lens*.

3. Draw a long vertical line a few inches to the right of the dot. Label it *film*.

4. Draw a straight line from X, through lens, to film.

5. Draw a straight line from Y, through lens, to film.

Observations

The straight line in steps 4 and 5 represent light going from object to film. The light must travel in a straight line and it must travel through the lens. Thus the light from X appears at the bottom, the light from Y appears at the top, and the image of XY appears upside down.

ELECTRICITY

■ STATIC ELECTRICITY

Purpose

The following experiments with static electricity (*static* refers to electricity that stays in one place) will demonstrate how objects can be electrically charged and how the charged objects react to one another. (Note: Do not do these experiments on days when the humidity is high.)

Apparatus

scissors
piece of fur or silk
small sheet of thin paper
plastic comb
2 balloons (inflated)

EXPERIMENT 1

Steps

1. Cut up the sheet of thin paper into tiny pieces and pile them on a table.

2. Hold the comb near the paper. Does anything happen?

3. Rub the comb briskly against the fur, then hold it near the paper again. What happens now?

Observations

The comb becomes electrically charged when rubbed and is thus capable of attracting light objects, like the pieces of paper. When unrubbed, it remains neutral and has no power to attract.

EXPERIMENT 2

Steps

1. Rub both balloons briskly against your hair, then try to bring the balloons together. How do they behave?

2. Hold the rubbed balloons about an inch from your hair. What happens?

Observations

There are two kinds of electricity—positive and negative. If you rub different substances together, one kind appears on the rubbed object, the other on the rubbing body. Thus the balloons have one kind of charge, your hair has another. Since like charges repel, the balloons stand away from each other. Since opposite charges attract, your hair is drawn to the balloon.

■ **CIRCUITS: OPENED, CLOSED, AND SHORT**

Purpose

Electricity that flows, instead of standing still, is called current electricity. In a closed circuit, electricity flows from the negative terminal of a generator (even a single cell is a generator), through a conductor, back to the generator again (this time to its positive terminal). You can regulate the flow of current—turn a light on or off, for instance—by using a switch to open or close the circuit. This process is interrupted, however, if a short circuit occurs—usually when insulation wears out and two wires touch each other. The following experiments will demonstrate the workings of a simple switch and the results of a short circuit.

Apparatus

42 inches of insulated copper bell wire
knife
2 tongue depressors
1 board, about 7 inches square, 1 inch thick
hammer and nails
1½-volt bulb and socket
No. 6 dry cell with screw terminals
pencil

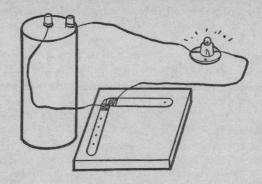

EXPERIMENT 1

Steps

1. Cut the wire into two 16-inch pieces and one 10-inch piece.

2. Use your knife to scrape 2 inches of insulation from each end of the 10-inch wire.

3. Do the following to both 16-inch wires: Scrape off 4 inches of insulation at one end and 2 inches at the other, then wrap the bared 4 inches of wire around one end of a tongue depressor. This will give you two wired depressors.

4. Place the depressors on the board at right angles to each other, with the wired ends forming an upper-left right angle. They should overlap slightly.

5. Hammer several nails into the vertical depressor below the line of wire, so that the depressor is held firmly in place.

6. Hammer one nail into the horizontal depressor at its unwired end, so that it is attached to the board, but free to move to and from the other depressor. (For the time being, move it up and away from the other depressor so that it no longer forms a right angle.)

7. The wire attached to the movable depressor should now be attached at its free end to a terminal of the light socket.

8. The wire attached to the fixed depressor should now be attached at its free end to a terminal of the dry cell.

9. Use the 10-inch wire to connect the other terminal of the dry cell and the other terminal of the light socket.

10. Now bring the end of your movable depressor in contact with the fixed depressor, making sure that the wires touch.

Observations

If all your connections are secure, the bulb will light. You have turned it on with your simple switch (the wired tongue depressors), which closed the circuit and allowed electric current to flow. To turn off the light, simply flip the movable part of the switch so that the wire contact is broken.

EXPERIMENT 2

Steps

1. With the apparatus in Experiment 1, use your switch to open the circuit to turn off the light.

2. Scrape 1 inch of insulation from the two wires connected to the dry cell. Be sure these wires do not touch each other.

3. Close the circuit with your switch and turn on the light.

4. Using the pencil, not your fingers, push together the bared sections of wire. What happens?

Observations

When the wires are pushed together, the electricity takes the short circuit from one wire to the other instead of traveling all the way around. As a result, no current passes through the bulb and it will not light.

■ SERIES AND PARALLEL CONNECTIONS

Purpose

There are two general methods of wiring an electric circuit —in series and in parallel. In a series connection of lights, the electricity passes, in turn, from bulb to bulb. In a parallel connection, the flow of electricity is divided, some of it going to one bulb while the rest continues on to the others. The following experiment will show how to make series and parallel connections and will demonstrate some facts about each method of wiring a circuit.

Apparatus

3 1½-volt bulbs and sockets
48 inches of insulated copper bell wire
knife
No. 6 dry cell with screw terminals
small screw driver

EXPERIMENT 1

Steps

1. Cut two 16-inch and two 4-inch pieces of wire. Scrape off 1 inch of insulation from both ends of each piece.

2. Screw the bulbs into the sockets and set them side by side in a semicircle.

3. Use a 4-inch wire (and the screwdriver) to connect the right terminal of socket 1 to the left terminal of socket 2. Use the other 4-inch wire to attach the right terminal of socket 2 to the left terminal of socket 3.

4. Connect the positive terminal of the dry cell to the left terminal of socket 1 with a 16-inch wire. Connect the negative terminal of the cell to the right terminal of socket 3 with the other 16-inch wire. All the bulbs will light.

5. Unscrew bulb 2. All the bulbs will go out.

6. Remove sockets 2 and 3 from the circuit. Disconnect the two 4-inch wires, and disconnect the 16-inch wire from socket 3. Let its other end remain attached to the cell.

7. Attach the free end of the 16-inch wire to the right terminal of socket 1 so that this socket is now attached to the cell by the two 16-inch wires. The remaining single bulb will burn more brightly than each of the three bulbs did in step 4.

Observations

In a series connection, when one bulb fails, all the bulbs go out. Since the bulbs in a series connection share equally in all the electricity, the fewer bulbs there are, the more brightly each one shines.

EXPERIMENT 2

Steps

1. Disconnect the four wires from the sockets and cell used in Experiment 1.

2. Cut two more 4-inch wires and bare 1 inch at the ends.

3. Set the three sockets side by side with their terminals to the front and rear.

4. Hook the rear terminals together with 4-inch wires between sockets 1 and 2, and 2 and 3.

5. Hook the front terminals together with 4-inch wires between sockets 1 and 2, and 2 and 3.

6. Attach the rear terminal of socket 1 to an end of the 16-inch wire. Attach the other end of wire to the negative terminal of the dry cell.

7. Attach the front terminal of socket 1 to an end of the other 16-inch wire. Attach the other end of wire to the positive terminal of the dry cell. The bulbs will light.

8. Unscrew one of the bulbs. What happens to the other bulbs?

9. Remove sockets 2 and 3 and all the 4-inch wires from the circuit, so that the only remaining bulb is the one connected by the 16-inch wires. Is the bulb brighter?

Observations

In a parallel connection, one burned-out or loosened bulb does not break the circuit—the other bulbs still light. Since each bulb is identical, each gets the same amount of electricity in a parallel connection, regardless of the number of bulbs in the circuit. Thus the removal of the two bulbs in step 9 does not affect the brightness of the one that remains.

■ THE LAWS OF MAGNETISM

Purpose

What objects are attracted to magnets? How can an object be magnetized? Can magnetic force flow through barriers? Six simple experiments will enable you to answer these and other questions about magnetism.

Apparatus

bar magnet with poles along the edges or at the ends
splinter of wood
steel needle
plastic comb
penny
iron filings
cloth
iron nail
sugar
piece of paper
steel paper clip
cork, ½ inch thick
soup bowl
water
knife
pencil

EXPERIMENT 1

Steps

1. Test the magnet on the following objects, each in turn: the penny, the splinter of wood, the needle, the plastic comb, the piece of paper, the cloth, the paper clip, the iron nail. Which are attracted to the magnet?

2. Mix together a spoonful of sugar and a spoonful of iron filings on the piece of paper. Move the magnet through the mixture. What happens?

Observations

Iron and steel objects are *strongly* attracted to magnets. Other metals, and all nonmetallic objects, are not. You can separate the sugar from the iron filings with the magnet. It will attract the filings, while the sugar remains behind.

Experiment 2

Steps

1. Stroke the needle from its center to an end with one of the poles of the magnet. Move only in one direction for 20 to 30 strokes.

2. Stroke the needle from its center to the other end, using the opposite pole of the magnet. Move only in one direction for 20 to 30 strokes.

3. See if the needle will now attract the paper clip and iron filings.

Observations

Steel or iron objects subjected to a magnetic field can become magnets.

Experiment 3

Steps

1. Break the magnet in half and use each, in turn, to attract the paper clip and the filings.

2. Bring a pole of one piece near a pole of the other. Do they pull together or push apart?

3. Turn one of the pieces around to its opposite pole and repeat step 2.

Observations

When a magnet is broken into smaller pieces, each piece becomes a complete magnet. Each magnet has a north and a south pole. Like poles repel; unlike poles attract.

Experiment 4

Steps

1. Use the knife to make a shallow-diameter gash across the top of the cork.

2. Place the needle—be sure it is magnetized—in the gash.

3. Fill the bowl almost to the brim with water, and float the cork on top. Note where the needle points.

4. Turn the cork or the bowl. Let the cork bob on the water until it settles. Where does the needle point?

Observations

The earth is a magnet, surrounded by a magnetic field which influences all other magnets. A free-floating magnetized needle (a simple compass) will always point north and south, attracted by the earth's magnetic poles.

EXPERIMENT 5

Steps

1. Place one of the bar magnets on the table and cover it with the paper.

2. Drop a pinch of iron filings onto the paper from a height of about 7 inches, then tap the paper with the pencil. What happens?

Observations

There is a field of force around a magnet which is called a magnetic field. When you tap the paper you cause the filings to map out this field.

EXPERIMENT 6

Steps

1. Place the paper clip on a table and cover it with the cloth.

2. Hold the magnet over the cloth, close to where the clip is located. Can you attract the clip to the magnet?

3. Place the paper clip on a table and cover it with a small piece of the paper.

4. Hold the magnet over the paper, close to where the clip is located. Can you attract the clip?

Observations

In this experiment magnetic force flowed through cloth and through paper. When strong enough, it can flow through any substance that the magnet does not attract.

■ ELECTROMAGNETISM

Purpose

There is an intimate relationship between electricity and magnetism. The following experiment will show how electric current can be used to make a magnet.

Apparatus

3-inch iron nail
35 inches of insulated copper bell wire
No. 6 dry cell with screw terminals
knife
5 paper clips
5 straight pins

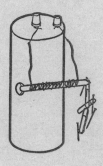

Steps

1. Coil the wire around the nail, leaving about 8 inches of uncoiled wire at each end.

2. Scrape 2 inches of insulation from both ends of the wire, and connect one piece to the positive terminal of the dry cell, the other to the negative terminal.

3. Try to attract the paper clips and straight pins with the wired nail. What happens?

4. Disconnect one of the wires from the dry cell. How does the nail behave now?

Observations

When electricity flows, it produces a magnetic field which magnetizes the nail. Thus the nail can attract the clips and pins. When you remove one of the wires from the dry cell, electric current no longer flows, and the nail is no longer a magnet.

■ **EXPLODING ATOMS**

Purpose

When radioactive substances disintegrate, they shoot out atomic particles. These tiny atomic explosions can be seen by doing the experiment below.

Apparatus

watch or clock with luminous dial
magnifying glass

Steps

1. Bring the clock into a pitch-black room and wait 10 minutes, until your eyes adjust to the dark.

2. Look at a number through the magnifying glass. Be sure it is close to the number and sharply focused.

Observations

The paint on the dial is composed of a small amount of a radioactive substance, which shoots out particles, and a larger amount of a fluorescent substance, whose molecules are hit by these particles. The collision results in flashes of light, which you can see through your magnifying glass.

MECHANICS

■ **GRAVITY**

Purpose

Mechanics is the study of forces and the effects of forces on bodies. One of the greatest forces is gravity—on our planet the constant pull of the earth on all objects that exist. Gravity pulls down on every particle of an object, and so the object's weight is, in fact, distributed. But each object has a point where, it seems, all its weight is concentrated. This point is called the center of gravity and it is there that an object can be balanced. In a regular-shaped object the center of gravity is located at its center. To find the center of gravity of an irregular-shaped object, do the experiment below.

Apparatus

sheet of cardboard
scissors
pencil
ruler
hammer and small headless nail
hole puncher
string
metal washer

Steps

1. Cut a figure with an irregular shape from the cardboard and make holes at various points around the edge with the hole puncher.

2. Hammer the headless nail part way into a wall and hang the figure from it by one of its holes.

3. Tie the washer to one end of the string. Tie the other end to the headless nail, so that the weighted string falls in a vertical line down the front of the cardboard. (Be sure the cardboard and string hang freely.) Use the ruler and pencil to mark this line on the figure.

4. Hang the figure from each of its other holes in turn, repeating step 3 each time.

5. Try to balance the figure on your finger at the point where all the lines intersect.

Observations

The figure will balance because you have located its center of gravity.

■ ACTION AND REACTION

Purpose

Force is a two-way proposition. If you exert force by pressing down on a table, the table will press back at your hand with equal force. A more obvious example is the rocket, which pushes upward because its fuel gases are pushing downward. In both cases an action produces an equal and opposite reaction. For a balloon-size demonstration of action and re-acton, try the simple experiment below.

Apparatus

balloon

Steps

1. Blow up the balloon, then pinch the neck with your fingers. Angle the balloon upward with your other hand.

2. Release your fingers to allow the air to begin rushing out; immediately afterward release the balloon.

Observations

The balloon will behave like a rocket, shooting through the room until all the air is expelled. The action of the air rushing out of the balloon produces an equal reaction in the opposite direction—the forward motion of the balloon.

■ INERTIA

Purpose

The tendency of a body at rest to remain at rest is called inertia. The tendency of a moving body to continue moving is also called inertia. To overcome the force of inertia, which is a resistance to change, an opposing force is needed. The following experiment will demonstrate inertia.

Apparatus

heavy book
cord
light string (just strong enough to support the book)
scissors

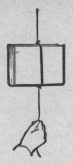

Steps

1. Tie the cord around the center of the book, passing it over the spine.

2. Attach a piece of the string to the section of cord passing over the spine; attach an equal piece of string to the opposite section of cord.

3. Suspend the book by one of the pieces of string. The other piece will hang below the book.

4. Give the lower string a quick jerk. It will break, leaving the book suspended.

5. Now pull down on the lower string (what is left of it) slowly and steadily. The upper string will break and the book will fall.

Observations

In step 4 the inertia of the book prevents the force of the quick jerk from reaching the upper string. In step 5 the steady application of force causes the book to move, so that the top string receives the force of both your pull and the book's weight.

■ MACHINES

Purpose

All work requires force, but force accomplishes work only when it moves a body. Machines make work easier by helping to exert force in a better way. Almost every machine that exists is a combination or a variation of six simple machines: the lever, pulley, wheel and axle, inclined plane, screw, and wedge. The following experiments will show how two of these machines operate.

Apparatus

block
yardstick
book
empty spool
piece of cord 10 inches long
piece of cord 8 feet long
strip of cloth, about 2 inches by 12 inches

EXPERIMENT 1

Steps

1. Lean the yardstick on the block (around the 13-inch mark) so that the longer section of stick touches the floor, the shorter section extends into the air.

2. Place the book on the end of the shorter section of the stick. That end will go down.

3. Press the other end of the stick with your little finger. The book will be lifted into the air.

Observations

The book is lifted by your little finger—and by the yardstick, which you have used as a lever. The block on which the yardstick sits is called the fulcrum, and the section of the yardstick between the block and your finger is called the effort arm. The longer the effort arm, the greater the weight that can be lifted. You can test this by lengthening the effort arm, then trying to lift a heavier book.

EXPERIMENT 2

Steps

1. Push the short piece of cord through the holes of the spool and tie the two ends together.

2. Suspend the spool by the cord from a nail or other support about 4 feet from the ground. Be sure the long part of the spool is horizontal.

3. Hang the other cord in the groove of the spool so the two ends hang at equal distances from the ground. Knot the ends.

4. Tie the cloth to the cord, about a foot up from the knot.

5. Pull down on the other side of the knot, until the cloth rises up to the spool.

Observations

You have just put to work a simple pulley—a grooved wheel with a rope that fits into the groove. Every flagpole has a pulley at the top, to enable flag raisers to raise the flag without having to climb up the pole.

PART 3
BIOLOGY

Biology is the study of all living things—amoeba and man, microscopic fungus and giant sequoia. Included in the biological sciences are botany, the study of plant life; zoology, the study of animal life; and human biology, the study of how our own bodies operate.

The basic unit in all living things, plant and animal, is the cell. The amoeba has only one cell; the human body has billions. If you know how to use a microscope and how to prepare slides, you can examine the cells of a plant (peel off the thin membrane present between two layers of an onion), the cells of an animal (tease a piece of membrane from the underside of some chicken skin), and your own cells (scrape off some of the lining on the inside of your cheek with the flat end of a clean toothpick). You will discover that all of these cells are different; yet all contain protoplasm, the substance of life.

In this section you will learn how a flower reproduces and how a leaf makes food; what conditions foster the development of bacteria; what changes the fruit fly undergoes in its growth from egg to adult; how your lungs and your senses operate. The living things to be examined represent only a tiny fraction of all life. Many of the processes and characteristics they exhibit, however, are applicable to billions of the eating and breathing, excreting and responding, reproducing and digesting plants and animals that populate our planet.

■ FLOWERS

Purpose

A green flowering plant is composed of four parts: flowers, leaves, stems, and roots. In this experiment you will investigate the structure and function of a typical flower by making a simple model.

Apparatus

2 pieces of heavy green paper
piece of heavy red paper
piece of heavy yellow paper
piece of heavy white paper
pencil
scissors
glue

Steps

1. The part of the stalk directly below the flower is called the receptacle. Growing from the top of the receptacle is a circle of leaflike structures called sepals, whose function is to protect the flower bud. (The entire circle of sepals is called the calyx.) Draw and cut out a model of the receptacle and the sepals from the green paper, using the illustration as your guide.

2. The most decorative part of the flower is its ring of petals, called the corolla, whose color and perfume attract insects. Draw and cut out a corolla from the red paper, using the illustration as your guide.

3. Inside the petals is a circle of stamens, composed of slender stalks (filaments) with bags of pollen (anthers) puffing out on top. Draw and cut out four or five stamens from the yellow paper, using the illustration as your guide.

4. The pistil, which looks a little like a bowling pin, stands inside the circle of stamens. Its rounded bottom is called the ovary, its sticky outer end is called the stigma, and its stalk is called the style. Draw and cut out a pistil from the green paper, using the illustration as your guide.

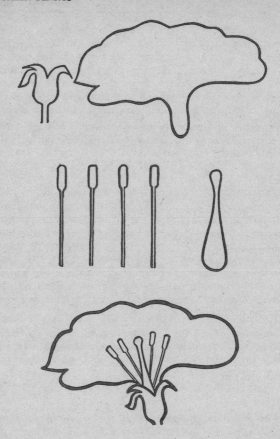

5. Glue the separate parts of the flower on the white paper as follows: Make a little slit in the lower center of the petals and slip the pistil and stamens inside, gluing them in place. Next glue the petals to the paper, and, finally, the calyx and receptacle. Use the illustration as your guide.

Observations

The chief function of the flower is to produce seeds, from which new plants will develop. In plant reproduction the stamens—the male parts of the flower—form pollen grains, which are carried by wind or insects to the pistil—the female part—of another flower. (A plant may also fertilize itself.) When pollen grains reach the stigma (the top of the pistil), each one grows a long pollen tube which stretches down into the ovary (the bottom of the pistil). Inside the ovary are ovules, and inside each ovule is an egg. A sperm formed by the pollen grain travels down the tube and unites with an egg. The ovule containing the fertilized egg grows into a seed, while the ovary develops into a fruit that contains the seed.

■ LEAVES

EXPERIMENT 1

Purpose

The leaves of green plants have a unique ability—they can make their own food. They take in carbon dioxide from the air and water from the ground and use the energy of the sun to convert these materials into sugar, and then into starch. This chemical reaction is known as photosynthesis. Leaves are able to make such use of sunlight, CO_2, and H_2O because they contain a green substance called chlorophyll. In the following experiment, certain aspects of photosynthesis will be demonstrated. (Note: Do this experiment in spring or summer.)

Apparatus

green house plant (We used a geranium plant.)
green-and-white coleus plant
black paper
scissors
paper clips
small beaker (150 milliliter)
water
20 milliliters of acetone
tweezers or tongs
3 small dishes
iodine
eye dropper
glass
electric hot plate

Steps

1. Cut a leaf-shaped piece from the black paper and clip it to a geranium leaf. Cover two other geranium leaves in this way.

2. Set the geranium plant and the coleus plant in the sun.

3. After 48 hours, cut off the three covered geranium leaves and remove the paper. Cut off three other geranium leaves and three coleus leaves.

4. Place the three once-covered geranium leaves in the beaker and cover the leaves generously with acetone. Let the leaves soak for a few minutes. To speed up, you may heat the mixture of leaves and acetone over an electric hot plate. CAUTION: use only electric heat.

5. Use the tweezers to pick the leaves from the beaker. Rinse them in water, then place them in one of the small dishes.

6. Repeat steps 4 and 5 with the other geranium leaves, and then with the coleus leaves, using the remaining two dishes.

7. Fill the glass with 6 ounces of water and add 20 drops of iodine. Pour ⅓ of this solution into each dish.

8. After 5 minutes, pour off the iodine solution and rinse the leaves. Compare the appearance of the leaves in the three dishes.

Observations

When you soaked the leaves in acetone you removed the chlorophyll. The acetone turned green, and the leaves became pale. They were now ready for the iodine test. Materials containing starch turn blue-black when treated with iodine. Three geranium leaves did not change color when treated with iodine because they had been covered by the black paper. Without light, green leaves cannot manufacture starch. The three geranium leaves exposed to the light were able to make starch. They turned blue-black. The coleus leaves were originally part white and part green. They were exposed to the light. When treated with iodine, only the part that was originally green turned blue-black. Without chlorophyll, leaves cannot manufacture starch.

EXPERIMENT 2

Purpose

The leaves of most green plants grow toward the light. This behavior, known as positive phototropism, can be observed by doing the following experiment.

Apparatus

green plant

Steps

1. Stand the plant on a window sill that receives sunlight most of the day.

2. After a week or more (depending on the amount of light), note any change in the plant.

3. Turn the plant so that its opposite side faces the sun. Repeat step 2.

Observations

The leaves of the plant bend in the direction of the light, changing position as the position of the plant shifts.

EXPERIMENT 3

Purpose

Plants take in carbon dioxide through microscopic openings, called stomates, located on the undersides of their leaves. What happens when carbon dioxide cannot enter a leaf? See the experiment below.

Apparatus

green house plant (We used a geranium plant.)
jar of Vaseline
paper towels

Steps

1. Smear the top sides of three leaves with Vaseline. (Do not remove the leaves from the plant.)

2. Smear the undersides of three other leaves with Vaseline. (Do not remove the leaves from the plant.)

3. After three days wipe off the Vaseline with the paper towels and compare the smeared leaves with one another and with the untreated leaves of the plant.

Observations

The leaves smeared on their top sides are still green and alive. Those smeared on their undersides, where the stomates are located, are yellow and dying. When the stomates are closed, no carbon dioxide can enter the leaves, and so they wither and die.

■ STEMS

Purpose

The stems of plants have numerous small tubes. These tubes carry water from roots to leaves, as the following experiment will show.

Apparatus

2 glasses
water
blue ink
white carnation
knife

Steps

1. Fill the glasses with water.

2. Add a teaspoon of ink to one glass, and stir.

3. With the knife slit the stem of the carnation vertically down the center from bottom to top.

4. Stand half the stem in one glass, the other half in the second glass. No liquid should touch the flower. After 24 hours observe the petals.

Observations

Half the carnation flower is flecked with blue, colored by the ink which traveled up through the tubes in the stem and into the petals.

■ ROOTS

EXPERIMENT 1

Purpose

Plants must have water in order to survive and grow. The following experiment will show that plant roots take in this needed water.

Apparatus

3 identical Impatiens plants (or other plant that quickly shows lack of water)
water
aluminum foil

Steps

1. Do not water the plant for three or four days.

2. When the plants begin to wilt, thoroughly water the soil of one plant.

3. Cover the soil of another plant with a piece of aluminum foil, so that no water can enter. Now thoroughly water the leaves.

4. Cover the soil of the third plant with aluminum foil, hold it sideways, and water only the stem.

5. After a few hours compare the appearance of the three plants.

Observations

The plant that received water only on its leaves continues to wilt, for the plant leaves cannot take in water. The plant that received water only on its stem continues to wilt, for plant stems cannot take in water. The plant with the watered soil is refreshed and healthy, for the water was taken in by the roots, and then traveled upward through the stems to the leaves.

EXPERIMENT 2

Purpose

The roots of plants are covered with numerous tiny, hairlike projections. These root hairs, as they are called, take in water and dissolved minerals from the soil by the process of osmosis. For a demonstration of osmosis, do the experiment below.

Apparatus

egg
knife
straight pin
plastic drinking straw, 6 inches long
stick of sealing wax
matches
drinking glass
water

Steps

1. With the knife and your fingernail, very carefully chip away a small portion of the shell on the larger end of the egg. Do not cut into the thin membrane beneath the shell.

2. On the opposite end of the egg make a small hole through both shell and membrane. (Use the straight pin to start the hole.) Push the straw through it, about ½ inch into the egg.

3. Light the end of the stick of sealing wax, let it burn for a few seconds, and then blow out the flame. Let the drippings fall onto the egg, around the straw. Do this several times, until the opening is sealed tightly. You will find this easier if you have a friend hold the egg while you supply the sealing wax.

4. Fill the glass ⅔ full of water and stand the egg in it, straw pointing upward. Let it stand for a day or two, until the contents of the egg begin to run out of the top of the straw.

Observations

Osmosis occurs when a weak solution (the water) is separated by a membrane from a strong solution (the material inside the egg). The water in the glass passes through the membrane into the egg, forcing the strong solution inside the egg to rise up in the straw. In the case of plants, each root hair is a projection of a cell, which, like the egg, contains strong solutions (protoplasm and cell sap). The soil water, which is a weaker solution, enters the root hairs by osmosis and passes upward through the plant. (Note: This experiment will not work if the membrane on the bottom of the egg is pierced, if there are any cracks in the egg, or if the seal at the top is not absolutely tight.)

■ BACTERIA

Purpose

The plant kingdom includes not only green plants, but colorless plants as well. Among these are bacteria—microscopic, single-celled, the smallest known forms of life. Bacteria can be observed by the naked eye only in the plural, as colonies growing on a food source. In the following experiments you will prepare such a food source and observe some bacteria behavior.

Apparatus

large pot with cover (a sterilizer is fine)
8 Petri dishes (bottoms and tops)
tongs
medium-sized pot
water
stove
1½ boxes of Knox gelatin (4 envelopes in each box)
bouillon cubes
salt
8 small cards or labels
sheet of paper
pencil
strand of hair
milk
piece of candy
eye dropper
soap

EXPERIMENT 1

Steps

1. Fill the large pot with water, place the Petri dishes and the tongs in the pot, and cover. (If necessary, use two pots.)

Boil on the stove for an hour to sterilize dishes and tongs, then turn off the flame.

2. Boil 2½ pints of water in the other pot and dissolve 4 envelopes of the gelatin in it. Stir in a bouillon cube until it dissolves, and add a tiny pinch of salt.

3. When the pot has cooled, remove the tongs, touching only the handle. Use the tongs to take the dishes from the pot, cover them, and set them in a warm dark place where they can remain undisturbed. Do not uncover until step 4.

4. Divide the gelatin-bouillon mixture equally among the eight dishes. Immediately cover the dishes. Do not touch the insides of the dishes with your fingers. Allow the gelatin to harden.

Observations

Bacteria cannot manufacture their own food; they must take it from plant or animal material such as the gelatin-bouillon mixture you have just prepared. When, in the next experiment, bacteria are introduced into this sterile culture medium, they will live and multiply.

Experiment 2

Steps

1. Number the cards from 1 to 8 and place one in front of each Petri dish. On the sheet of paper number from 1 to 8 and record what you do to each dish.

2. Leave dish 1 untouched.

3. Remove the cover of dish 2 and touch your finger lightly to the surface of the gelatin without breaking the surface. Promptly replace the cover.

4. Repeat step 3 with dishes 3 to 7, using—in turn—the point of the pencil, the hair, a drop of the water, a drop of the milk, and the candy.

5. Wash your hands thoroughly with soap and water, then touch a finger to dish 8. Don't break the surface. Promptly replace the cover.

6. After four days remove the covers from the dishes and examine the surface of the gelatin in each dish. Record their appearance on the sheet of paper.

Observations

Bacteria are everywhere, on your fingers and your hair, on the pencil, on the water and the milk, on the candy. When these objects are touched to the gelatin, bacteria stick to the surface and multiply rapidly, so that millions of them appear on the gelatin's surface as visible colonies of gray-white spots. Dish 1 shows no bacteria colonies because none were introduced to its sterile surface. Dish 8 shows little or no bacteria growth because the soap and water cleansed them from your finger. (Note: If hairy or colored growths also appear on the gelatin, these may very likely be molds rather than bacteria.)

Experiment 3

Steps

1. Throw the contents of the Petri dishes in the garbage, wash all equipment carefully with soap and water, and wash your hands thoroughly.

2. Sterilize three Petri dishes and fill them with a gelatin-bouillon mixture. Prepare about half the amount prepared in Experiment 1.

3. When the gelatin cools, touch the surface of the gelatin in each dish with the pencil point, then cover the dishes promptly.

4. Put one covered dish in the sunlight, another in the refrigerator and the third in a warm, dark place.

5. After four days remove the covers from the dishes and examine the surface of the gelatin in each dish. Record your observations.

6. Repeat step 1.

Observations

Bacteria grow best in warm dark places. Thus the bacteria grown in the sun and in the refrigerator multiply less rapidly than those grown in a more favorable environment.

■ YEASTS

Purpose

Yeasts are microscopic, one-celled plants that lack chlorophyll. They feed on sugar, producing from it alcohol and carbon dioxide in a process known as fermentation. Learn about yeasts by doing the experiments below.

Apparatus

3 water glasses
water
sugar
½ yeast cake
test tube
limewater
three labels
pencil

EXPERIMENT 1

Steps

1. Fill the glasses ⅔ full of water.

2. Dissolve 3 teaspoons of sugar in one glass, label it A, and set it in a warm place.

3. Mix ¼ of a yeast cake into the second glass, label it B, and set it in a warm place.

4. In the third glass dissolve 3 teaspoons of sugar and mix in ¼ of a yeast cake. Label this glass C, and set it in a warm place.

5. After three days examine and compare the glasses.

Observations

Glass A contains no yeast. Glass B contains no yeast food. Thus fermentation cannot take place. In glass C, however, the yeast feeds on the sugar and fermentation occurs. The smell of alcohol is apparent, and bubbles appear in this glass. To prove that the bubbles are carbon dioxide, do the next experiment.

EXPERIMENT 2

Steps

1. Fill the test tube with some of the fermented material from glass C.

2. Invert the test tube into the remaining liquid in the glass and set it aside.

3. After several hours the gas will drive the liquid from the test tube. Remove the test tube from the glass.

4. Pour an ounce of clear limewater into the test tube of gas and shake. What happens to the limewater?

Observations

The limewater turns milky. This change occurs only in the presence of carbon dioxide; thus the gas produced in fermentation must be CO_2.

■ MOLDS

Purpose

Molds, like bacteria and yeasts, are fungus plants. They lack chlorophyll and so must take their food from materials such as bread and fruit and cheese, leather and cloth. Molds are microscopic, but when great quantities of them develop they can be seen. Below are instructions for growing molds and studying the conditions best suited for their survival.

Apparatus

bread
dust
water
3 jars with covers

EXPERIMENT 1

Steps

1. Moisten a piece of bread and place some dust on top of it.

2. Pour a little water into the bottom of one of the jars, swish it around, and pour it out. Place the bread in the jar.

3. Close the jar and set it in a warm dark place.

4. After three days examine the bread.

Observations

A fluffy, furlike growth appears on the bread. It may be white or gray, blue or pink—or a combination of these colors—perhaps dotted with little black balls, called spores. This growth is a bread mold. Spores of the mold are present in the dust. When given proper conditions for growth, molds develop from the spores, and soon produce new spores of their own.

EXPERIMENT 2

Steps

1. Repeat steps 1 and 2 of Experiment 1, using the second jar. Close it and set it in the refrigerator.

2. Place a dry piece of bread in the third jar. Add no water to the jar. Close it and set it in a warm dark place.

3. After three days examine the pieces of bread in the jars. Compare them to the bread in Experiment 1.

Observations

Molds grow best when they have warmth, moisture and darkness. The bread in the second jar shows no mold growth because of its cold environment. The bread in the third jar shows no mold growth because it was not moist.

ANIMAL BIOLOGY

■ ONE-CELLED ANIMALS: PROTOZOA

Purpose

The animal kingdom has been divided and subdivided into many categories. One of the basic distinctions is between one-celled animals, called Protozoa, and animals of more than one cell, called Metazoa. The following experiment is a study of Protozoa, the simplest animals.

Apparatus

large container of pond water (When you obtain the water, be sure to include some of the surface scum.)
8-ounce jar
small handful of hay, loosely packed (If no hay is available, use dried grass or weeds. Do not use green material.)
square of cheesecloth
rubber band
5 grains of uncooked rice
boiled lettuce leaf
eye dropper
small quantity of absorbent cotton
2 slides

2 cover slips
microscope
pencil and paper

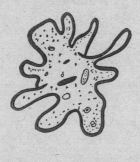 

Steps

1. Fill the jar ⅓ full of the pond water, including the scum.

2. Add the hay to the jar and cover with the cheesecloth, held in place with the rubber band. Stand the jar in a warm place.

3. After three days add the rice to the jar. Break up the lettuce leaf and add it also.

4. Let the jar stand in a warm place, covered with the cheesecloth, for another three days. There will be an increase in surface scum and an odor of decay.

5. Use the eye dropper to take up some of the pond water from the bottom of the jar. Try not to disturb the liquid. Place one drop on the slide.

6. Immediately pull out a few fibers from the cotton and drop them into the water on the slide, to confine some of the Protozoa. Cover the slide with the cover slip.

7. Look at the drop through the microscope and sketch some of the moving animals that you see. Try to identify them by comparing your sketches with illustrations in zoology books.

8. Repeat steps 5 to 7, this time using pond water taken from the top of the jar. (Note: Observe specimens between the sixth and tenth days. After that time there will probably be a decreasing number of Protozoa.)

Observations

The material you assembled in the jar is called a hay infusion. Protozoa present in the pond water multiply in the infusion because bacteria feed on the decaying rice and lettuce, and Protozoa, in turn, feed on the bacteria. Among the many species of Protozoa, two of the most common are the irregular-shaped amoeba and the paramecium, with its tiny, hairlike projections (cilia). Do you see either of these through the microscope? You may find that the species of Protozoa living at the bottom of the jar are different from those at the top.

■ INVERTEBRATES: THE EARTHWORM

Purpose

Animals in the Metazoa (multicellular) category are divided into two groups: invertebrates (animals without backbones) and vertebrates (animals with backbones). The earthworm will be studied below as an example of invertebrate animals.

Apparatus

bowl
2 large water glasses
dark, fertile soil
2 tablespoons of dry breakfast cereal
2 lcttucc lcavcs
6 earthworms from a yard
water
aluminum foil
several straight pins
large, 6-inch earthworm (Obtain it from a biological supply house.)
cardboard
strong hand lens
single-edge razor blade

EXPERIMENT 1

Steps

1. Measure out ½ glass of soil and pour it into the bowl. Add the cereal and mix well.

2. Fill each water glass as follows: ¼ glass of plain soil, three worms on top of the soil, ¼ glass of soil-cereal mixture on top of the worms. Do not pack down the soil.

3. Shred the lettuce leaves and place them on top of the soil-cereal mixture in each glass.

4. Moisten—do not flood—the soil in one glass. Cover with aluminum foil, and punch holes in the top with the pin.

5. Do not add any water to the other glass. Cover with aluminum foil and punch holes in the top.

6. Set the two glasses in a dark place. Keep the soil moistened in the one glass only. Observe the behavior of the worms over the course of several days.

Observations

Earthworms are dependent on moisture for survival; thus the worms in the dry soil will die within a short time. The worms in the other jar should survive, however. They will feed on the dirt and the food, and make tunnels in the moist soil.

EXPERIMENT 2

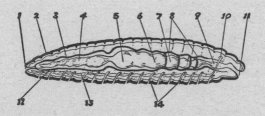

Steps

1. Study the large earthworm with the hand lens. Examine its external appearance. Locate its head and tail and note the way its body is constructed.

2. Dissect the worm by cutting it lengthwise with the razor blade down the center of its back.

3. Using the straight pins, pin the worm open on the cardboard.

4. Using the hand lens, examine its internal structure and compare it with the illustration. How many parts of the body can you identify?

Observations

The head of the worm is larger than the tail, round instead of pointed. Its body is segmented—divided into separate sections. The thickened area you see is the egg case, called the clitellum. When you dissect the worm, you will see that it has no backbone. The structures you observe (you probably won't locate all of them) should match those numbered in the illustration: (1) anus, (2) body wall, (3) dorsal blood vessel, (4) intestine, (5) gizzard, (6) crop, (7) esophagus, (8) hearts, (9) pharynx, (10) brain, (11) mouth, (12) ventral blood vessel, (13) ventral nerve cord, (14) excretory tubes.

■ VERTEBRATES: THE GOLDFISH

Purpose

The goldfish is an easy-to-work-with example of a vertebrate, an animal with a backbone. Like all true fish, it has scales and fins, is cold-blooded and breathes with gills. Like all vertebrates, it has a well-defined circulatory system. See the experiment below.

Apparatus

goldfish in bowl
cotton
fish net
2 slides
microscope

Steps

1. Dip the cotton into the fish bowl until it is thoroughly soaked.

2. Use the net to remove the goldfish from the water. Immediately wrap it in the wet cotton, covering everything but the tail. (If you handle the fish carefully, it should survive this experiment very nicely.)

3. Set the wrapped fish under the microscope, with one slide under the tail; cover with another slide so that the movement of the fish will not spoil the focus. Observe the tail through the microscope. As soon as you have seen the movement of blood through its tail, return the fish to the bowl.

Observations

You will see the blood vessels carrying blood from the head section into the tail, then back from the tail to the head. As the blood circulates through the body of the fish, it brings food and oxygen to all the cells and carries waste products away.

■ LIFE CYCLE: THE FRUIT FLY

Purpose

The life cycle of an animal is the various changes it under-goes during its lifetime. The fruit fly, for example, passes through four distinct stages: egg, larva, pupa, and adult. In the following experiments you will collect fruit flies and study the four stages in their life cycle.

Apparatus

2 small pieces of white paper
2 glass jars (1 with a cover)
ripe banana
cotton
hand lens

EXPERIMENT 1

Steps

1. Place a piece of paper on the bottom of each jar, and put a slice of banana on top of each piece of paper. Cover one jar tightly.

2. Stand both the closed and open jars outside for 24 hours (any season except winter).

3. Observe and compare the jars, then loosely plug the mouth of the open jar with cotton.

Observations

Fruit flies appear in and around the open jar. (The plug of cotton will keep them confined for the next experiment.) No flies appear in or around the closed jar. According to an old theory of spontaneous generation, fruit flies came from rotting fruit. This experiment shows that rotting food is surrounded with the flies only when exposed to air. The fruit flies came from eggs deposited in the nearby area.

EXPERIMENT 2

Steps

1. Use the hand lens to help you observe the adult fruit flies in the cotton-plugged jar. Can you distinguish the males from the females?

2. Check the bottom of the jar and note when eggs are deposited. What are the color and size of the eggs?

3. The larva stage occurs a few days after the eggs appear. Can you tell when the larva stage ends and the pupa stage begins?

4. Watch for the appearance of the adult fruit flies. How long did it take for the flies to develop from eggs to adults?

Observations

The male fruit fly is smaller than the female and has a black-tipped abdomen. The eggs are white and very tiny. The larvae emerge from the eggs and wiggle about, then crawl onto the paper to become immobile pupae. The adult fruit fly emerges from the pupa about ten or twelve days after the egg was laid.

■ HEREDITY: MENDEL'S LAW

Purpose

In the 19th century Gregor Mendel discovered some basic laws of heredity. He found that certain characteristics—like tallness or blondness—are inherited as independent units. When two conflicting characteristics—like pure blackness and pure whiteness—are inherited, one is dominant (black) and one is recessive (white). The result is a hybrid, which appears black but carries the white characteristic in its genes. What happens when first-generation hybrids mate? See the experiment below.

Apparatus

4 black checkers
4 white checkers

Steps

1. Pile one black checker on top of another black checker. Pile one white checker on top of another white checker.

2. Combine a checker from each pile to make a new pile. Whenever black and white combine, black must be on top because it is the dominant color. Make two black-and-white piles.

3. Using the two prepared piles in step 2, work out the four possible ways in which a checker from one black-and-white pile can combine with a checker from another black-and-white pile.

Observations

Black can combine with black once. White can combine with white once. Black can combine with white twice. If the checkers were guinea pigs, there would be three black offspring to one white. The white guinea pig would be pure white, one black would be pure, and the other two black guinea pigs would be hybrids.

HUMAN BIOLOGY

■ THE DIGESTIVE SYSTEM

Purpose

The digestive system is composed of the mouth, the esophagus, the stomach, and the small and large intestines. It also includes glands which manufacture enzymes, whose chemical action breaks down proteins, fats, and carbohydrates into simple substances that can be carried by the blood stream. In the following experiments you will see how enzymes in the mouth convert starch into simple sugar.

Apparatus

boiled potato, cut into thirds
iodine
eye dropper
water
glass
small pot
Benedict's solution

EXPERIMENT 1

Steps

1. Bite into a piece of the potato and chew it for a minute. Do not swallow.

2. Place the chewed potato in the pot, add 2 tablespoons of Benedict's solution and half a glass of water. Boil for 5 minutes. What happens to the color of the solution?

EXPERIMENT 2

Steps

1. In the glass prepare an iodine solution of 4 ounces of water and 20 drops of iodine.

2. Break up another piece of the potato and add it to the glass of iodine solution. What happens to the color of the potato?

EXPERIMENT 3

Steps

1. Wash the pot thoroughly. Break up the remaining piece of potato into the pot, add 2 tablespoons of Benedict's solution and half a glass of water.

2. Boil the mixture for 5 minutes. What happens to the color of the solution?

EXPERIMENT 4

Steps

1. Rinse your mouth thoroughly with water. Wash the pot. Place some of your own saliva in the pot, and add 2 tablespoons of Benedict's solution and half a glass of water.

2. Boil the mixture for 5 minutes. What happens to the color of the solution?

Observations

When, in Experiment 1, you tested the chewed potato for the presence of sugar, the solution turned orange—a positive reaction. In Experiment 2 the unchewed potato was tested for the presence of starch and turned blue—a positive reaction. In Experiment 3 the unchewed potato was tested for sugar and the solution showed no color change. In Experiment 4 your saliva was tested for sugar and the solution showed no color change. Thus an unchewed potato, and your own saliva, contain no sugar. When the saliva acts on the potato, however, a chemical change occurs—the enzymes in the saliva convert the starch in the potato to sugar. You can see now why it is important to chew food well. Chewing breaks down food into a large number of surface areas, enabling the saliva to mix with it thoroughly and making the food easier to digest.

■ THE RESPIRATORY SYSTEM

Purpose

The cells of the body need oxygen to convert food to energy. Air, which contains oxygen, enters the windpipe through the mouth or nose, passes into the two bronchial tubes and then into the lungs. In the lungs are air sacs containing blood vessels, which receive the oxygen from the air and discharge carbon dioxide. The following experiment will demonstrate how human beings inhale and exhale air.

Apparatus

bell jar
1-hole rubber stopper to fit jar
Y-tube to fit stopper
2 small, identical balloons
4 rubber bands
large balloon
scissors

Steps

1. Push the stopper into the opening of the bell jar. Be sure it fits tightly.

2. Push the Y-tube into the stopper's hole, so that the two prongs of the tube hang into the jar.

3. Place a small balloon on the end of each prong, and hold each in position with a rubber band.

4. Cut a piece of rubber from the large balloon. It should be big enough to fit over the opening of the bell jar. Use the two remaining rubber bands to attach the rubber sheet to the opening.

5. Grasp the center of the rubber sheet and pull down on it. What happens to the balloons?

6. Grasp the center of the rubber sheet and push up on it. What happens to the balloons?

Observations

The two balloons represent the lungs; the rubber sheet represents the diaphragm; the tube represents the windpipe; the bell jar represents the rib cage. When we inhale, the diaphragm moves downward. The air pressure inside the rib cage is lowered, and the greater outside pressure pushes air through the windpipe into the lungs. Thus the lungs—the balloons—inflate. When we exhale, the pressure is greater inside, and air is forced out of the lungs and the windpipe. Thus the lungs—the balloons—deflate. (Note: In actual breathing, the rib cage—the bell jar—also participates by expanding when we inhale.)

■ THE CIRCULATORY SYSTEM

Purpose

Blood contains oxygen and dissolved food, which must be carried to all the cells of the body. It also contains dissolved wastes, which must be carried to organs that dispose of them. The circulatory system—the heart and a network of blood vessels—takes care of the movement of the blood. In the following experiments you will explore the circulatory system by examining blood cells, heartbeat, and pulse.

Apparatus

needle
matches

97% ethyl alcohol, or rubbing alcohol
cotton ball
2 slides
microscope
rubber tubing, 2 feet long
metal funnel
roll of adhesive tape
clock with second hand

Experiment 1

Steps

1. Sterilize the needle with the flame of a match. Pour some alcohol onto the cotton ball and clean the tip of your left forefinger by rubbing it with the cotton.

2. Squeeze your forefinger between thumb and second finger. Quickly jab the needle into your finger, just deep enough to cause bleeding. (Have a qualified adult supervisor standing by during this part of the experiment, to make sure that the conditions are sufficiently antiseptic. Do not do this experiment without asking permission from a parent.)

3. Squeeze the stuck finger and let a large drop of blood fall onto the end of a slide. Use a second slide to smear the blood thinly from end to end of the first slide, then observe the smear under the microscope. As soon as you have prepared the slide, and before you look at it, clean your finger again with the alcohol.

Observations

You will see red and possibly white blood cells under the microscope. The red cells will appear pink, and will be smaller and far more numerous than the whites. The red blood cells carry oxygen; the whites fight harmful bacteria. Lymph, the watery part of the blood, carries foods and wastes.

Experiment 2

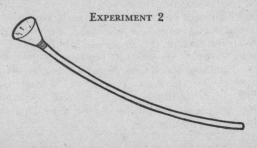

Steps

1. Attach one end of the rubber tubing to the tube of the funnel.

2. If necessary, wrap adhesive tape around the juncture of tubing and funnel to make a tight attachment.

3. Place the funnel on a friend's chest, over the heart.

4. While the friend holds the funnel, you hold the open end of the tube to your ear with one hand. Cover your other ear with your other hand, and listen to the sound in the tube.

Observations

You will hear the beating of your friend's heart. The funnel amplifies the sound, and your covered ear is sheltered from other sounds that might interfere with the reception. The heart is divided into four chambers—two upper (auricles) and two lower (ventricles). The left auricle receives blood from the lungs, the right auricle receives blood from the rest of the body. The right ventricle pumps blood to the lungs, the left ventricle pumps blood to the rest of the body. The blood circulates from right auricle to right ventricle, into the lungs, then into the left auricle and left ventricle. Heartbeats are contractions of the left ventricle muscles.

EXPERIMENT 3

Steps

1. Place two fingers on the pulse on the inner side of your wrist and count the number of beats you feel in 60 seconds.

2. Touch your toes, run quickly up and down stairs, or do some other exercise for a minute or two. Now take your pulse again.

Observations

Veins carry blood to the heart; arteries carry blood away from the heart. When the blood is pushed into the arteries, the arteries stretch. Pulse rate is the number of these stretches occurring in 60 seconds. In step 1 you took your pulse under normal conditions. Step 2 shows that strenuous activity increases pulse rate.

■ THE FIVE SENSES

Experiment 1

Purpose

The following experiment will demonstrate that sensitivity to touch varies, depending on the part of the body that is contacted.

Apparatus

2 identical nails
small piece of cardboard

Steps

1. Push the nails into the cardboard, about ½ inch apart.

2. Ask a friend to close his eyes. Touch the back of his neck with the points of the nails. What does he feel?

3. Ask your friend to close his eyes and hold out his hand. Gently touch the tip of his finger with the points of the nails. What does he feel?

Observations

Your friend will feel the point of one nail in step 2, but will feel two nails in step 3. The finger tip has more touch receptors than the back of the neck does, and so is more sensitive to touch.

Experiment 2

Purpose

This experiment will test variations in hearing ability.

Apparatus

clock
yardstick

Steps

1. In a perfectly quiet room, hold the clock next to a friend's ear, then slowly move away in a straight line.

2. Ask your friend to tell you when he can no longer hear the ticking of the clock. Measure the distance from that point to where he is standing.

3. Repeat steps 1 and 2 with his other ear, then ask him to test your hearing in the same way.

Observations

It is possible that you will find that you and your friend have different hearing abilities, and that there are even differences between the hearing abilities of the left and right ears.

Experiment 3

Purpose

This experiment will show the relationship between the sense of smell and the sense of taste. It will also show that there are only four tastes which the tongue can recognize without the assistance of the nose.

Apparatus

peppermint chewing gum
sugar
salt
lemon
aspirin
4 glasses
water

Steps

1. Ask a friend to close his eyes and hold his nose. Put the gum in his mouth and tell him to chew it. Can he taste the peppermint flavor? Tell him to stop holding his nose and continue chewing. Can he taste the peppermint now?

2. Fill the four glasses with water. Add a teaspoon of sugar to one, a teaspoon of salt to another, squeeze half a lemon into the third, and dissolve the aspirin into the fourth.

3. Ask your friend to close his eyes and hold his nose. Have him take a sip, in turn, from each glass. How many tastes can he distinguish?

Observations

Your friend will not recognize the peppermint flavor as long as he holds his nose. The taste of the peppermint is due to its aroma. However, the taste buds of the tongue can recognize the four tastes of the liquids prepared in step 2— sweet, salty, sour, and bitter.

EXPERIMENT 4

Purpose

For a split second after you stop viewing an object, its image remains on your retina. The following experiment will demonstrate the phenomenon of the afterimage.

Apparatus

black paper
white paper
scissors
paste

Steps

1. Cut out a circle from the black paper.

2. Cut two smaller circles from the white paper and paste them on the black circle.

3. Hold the black circle under a bright light and stare at it for a minute. Then lift your gaze to a blank wall that is only dimly lit. What do you see?

Observations

The circular design will appear on the wall with the big circle white and small circles black.

EXPERIMENT 5

Purpose

The human eye can distinguish size, depth, and distance, as well as color and form. But seeing is not always believing, for the eye can be tricked. The following experiment will demonstrate optical illusions.

Apparatus

pencil and paper
ruler

Steps

1. Draw a four-sided figure with these dimensions: top, 2 inches; bottom, 3 inches; left and right, 1¼ inches. Top and bottom should be parallel. Below this figure draw another figure with these dimensions: top, 2 inches; bottom, 1 inch; left and right, 1¼ inches. Top and bottom should be parallel. Compare the appearance of the top lines.

2. Draw a 4-inch square. In the center draw a 1-inch square. Draw a line from the upper left corner of the small square to the upper left corner of the big square. Draw a line from the lower left corner of the small square to the lower left corner of the big square. Draw a line from the upper right corner of the small square to the upper right corner of the big square. Draw a line from the lower right corner of the small square to the lower right corner of the big square. Look at the figure. Can you see two views of it?

3. Look at the three figures in the illustration. What is the optical illusion of each figure?

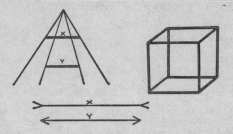

Observations

The top lines of the figures drawn in step 1 are identical, but the line in the first appears longer than the line in the second. The inner square of the figure drawn in step 2 appears to be forward sometimes, rearward other times. In the upper left figure shown in the illustration, line X appears longer than line Y, but they are actually identical. The same is true of the lower left figure. The figure on the right displays two views—sometimes appearing to be the top of a cube, sometimes the bottom.

PART 4
WEATHER

Weather is determined by many conditions—by the pressure of the air and the moisture that is in it, by the sun and by the winds. The endless interaction of these factors is responsible for everything from the blazing, humid days of summertime to winter's bitter snows and freezing temperatures.

By coming to understand the circumstances that produce blizzards and heat waves, scientists have permanently removed weather prediction from the realm of aching corns and ground-hogs' shadows. Precise instruments observing and tabulating weather conditions all over the world enable meteorologists to recognize a pattern in today's weather and to anticipate what tomorrow will bring.

The experiments presented here will demonstrate some of the whys of weather and will show you how to construct simple weather instruments. If you wish, you can keep daily records of barometric pressure, relative humidity, amount of rainfall, etc., and try some predictions of your own.

You will find, as you make your observations, that there are no such things as an "inexplicable" drop in temperature or a storm "coming out of nowhere." For behind these—and all the kinds of weather that exist—are orderly and logical processes of nature, processes that have been repeated and repeated since the beginning of time.

■ AIR IS MATTER

Purpose

It is impossible to understand weather without understanding air. And the first thing to understand about air is that it is matter—it has weight and it occupies space. The following experiments will demonstrate these two fundamental characteristics of air.

EXPERIMENT 1

Apparatus

12-inch ruler
drill
knife
3 pieces of string
2 balloons, same size, uninflated

Steps

1. Drill a hole above the 6-inch mark on the ruler, close to the upper edge.

2. With the knife, notch the ruler above the 1-inch mark and above the 11-inch mark.

3. Tie one of the strings through the hole and suspend the ruler from a table edge or shelf.

4. Tie a balloon to each of the other two strings, tie the strings into loops of equal size, and loop one of them over each notch. The ruler should be in balance. (If it is not, adjust the balloons until they are balanced on the ruler.)

5. Remove one of the balloons and blow it up. Return it to its place on the string and put the string on the ruler again, exactly where it was before. Is the ruler still balanced?

Observations

The ruler no longer balances because the air-filled balloon is heavier than the empty balloon. This experiment shows that air has weight.

Experiment 2

Apparatus

    pan
    water
    water glass
    piece of paper

Steps

1. Fill the pan ⅔ full of water.

2. Crumple the paper and fit it securely into the bottom half of the glass.

3. Turn the glass upside down and push it into the pan of water. (Be sure the paper stays in the same position.) Hold it there for a couple of minutes, then remove the glass and look at the paper.

Observations

The paper remains dry. Water does not fill the entire glass because the seemingly empty space in the glass is already occupied—by air.

■ AIR EXERTS PRESSURE

Purpose

Air is continuously pressing down on earth, and its pressure is an important determinant of our weather. For a vivid demonstration that air does, indeed, exert pressure, do the following experiment.

Apparatus

    gallon can with flat sides and stopper
    water
    stove
    pot holder

Steps

1. Fill the can with about 1 inch of water.

2. Set the can on the stove without the stopper, and boil the water for several minutes.

3. With the pot holder remove the can from the stove and replace the stopper securely.

4. Cool the can—either wait until it cools by itself or stand it in the sink and run cold water on it.

5. Observe the can as it cools. Its sides will collapse, as if some giant force has battered them in.

Observations

The powerful force that crushed the can is air pressure. The steam inside the can condensed as it cooled, forming a partial vacuum. The air outside the can exerted much more pressure than the air within, and so the can collapsed.

■ MEASURING AIR PRESSURE: THE BAROMETER

Purpose

A barometer is a scientific instrument that measures air pressure at a particular point. Below are instructions for making a simple version of this valuable weather-casting tool.

Apparatus

tin can, open at one end
balloon
rubber band
scissors
glue
straw from a broom
transparent tape
piece of paper, about 2 inches wide and twice the height of
  the can
pencil

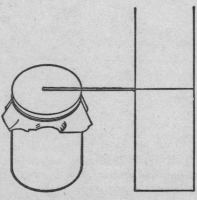

Steps

1. Cut a square from the balloon and stretch it over the open end of the can to make a diaphragm. Hold it in place by wrapping the rubber band around the overlap.

2. Place the straw on the rubber diaphragm so that it extends horizontally from the diaphragm's center to an inch or two beyond the edge. Glue it securely.

3. Tape the piece of paper (longer dimension vertical) to a wall. It should be near the floor or above a shelf, away from radiators and direct sunlight. Place the can beside it. Arrange paper and can so that the free end of the straw touches the paper about halfway down from the top. Draw a line across the paper at this point.

4. Observe the straw over the course of several days. Changes in air pressure will cause it to move up or down on the paper.

Observations

When the air pressure on the outside of the diaphragm is greater than the pressure inside the can, the diaphragm—and the part of the straw attached to the center of the diaphragm—are depressed. When the straw is pushed down at the center it moves upward at the end, where it touches the paper. Rising barometric pressure generally means fair weather. When the straw moves down on the paper, however, barometric pressure is falling, and the weather will change or turn bad.

MOISTURE

■ EVAPORATION

Purpose

Some moisture is always present in the air. Water enters the air by evaporation, by changing from a liquid to a gas (water vapor). Water is constantly evaporating from rivers and oceans, from the ground, from clothes drying on the line. Demonstrations of evaporation follow.

Apparatus

12-inch ruler
drill
knife
3 pieces of string
2 paper cups, same size
soil
assorted objects
stick
water
drinking glass
adhesive tape
2 pieces of cloth, same size
electric fan

EXPERIMENT 1

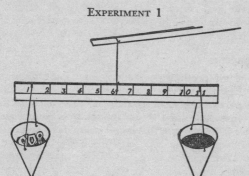

Steps

1. Drill a hole above the 6-inch mark on the ruler, close to the upper edge.

2. With the knife, notch the ruler above the 1-inch mark and above the 11-inch mark.

3. Tie one of the strings through the hole and use it to suspend the ruler from the stick. Then suspend the stick from a table edge or shelf so that the ruler swings freely.

4. Make two holes near the top of each paper cup, one hole directly opposite the other. Tie a string through each pair of holes in a loose loop.

5. Loop one cup over the ruler at the 1-inch mark, the other over the ruler at the 11-inch mark. The cups should be in balance.

6. Fill one cup halfway with well-moistened soil and fill the other cup with the assorted objects until the cups are again in balance.

7. After 24 hours check the cups. Are they still balanced on the ruler?

EXPERIMENTS 2, 3, AND 4

Steps

1. Fill the glass ¾ full of water and mark the water line with adhesive tape (or other practical substitute). Let the glass stand undisturbed for 24 hours. What happens to the water line?

2. Wet both pieces of cloth. Let one dry at normal room temperature; dry the other by turning the fan on it. Which piece dries first?

3. Pour water on your hand and wave it in the air. Does your hand feel cooler or warmer as it dries?

Observations

Water evaporates from the soil—the cups become unbalanced. Water evaporates from the glass—the water line falls. Evaporation is speeded by moving air—the fan-dried cloth dries faster. When water evaporates from a surface, heat is removed from that surface—your hand feels cooler.

■ RAIN

Purpose

Warm air can hold more moisture than cool air can. When warm air up in the sky is cooled, the water vapor it contains condenses into tiny droplets, forming a cloud. If cooling continues, the drops increase in size, become too heavy for the air to hold, and fall to earth as rain. The following experiments will demonstrate this process and will show how you can measure the amount of rain that falls.

EXPERIMENT 1

Apparatus

stove
kettle
metal baking pan
ice cubes
water

Steps

1. Fill the kettle part way with water and set it on the stove to boil.

2. Place the ice cubes in the metal pan.

3. Hold the pan above the kettle's spout, so that it is struck by the cloud of steam which comes out of the spout. What happens?

Observations

The hot moist air from the kettle is cooled when it leaves the spout. Water vapor condenses, forming a cloud. The cloud is then cooled by the icy pan, and the droplets of water within the cloud grow larger, until it begins to "rain."

EXPERIMENT 2

Apparatus

large fruit-juice can or other metal container with perfectly
    vertical sides and a flat bottom, top removed
ruler
water
narrow glass jar with vertical sides, flat bottom
strip of paper 1 inch wide, same height as glass jar
glue
pencil
funnel

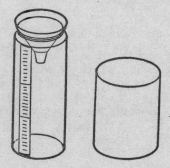

Steps

(*Note: The can, with its top removed, will serve as a rain collector. But before you collect any rain, you must devise a precise way of measuring it. Instructions follow.*)

1. Fill the can with water to the height of 1 inch. Use your ruler to measure the height of the water accurately.

2. Pour this inch of water into the jar. Glue the strip of paper down the side of the jar and mark the water level on the strip with a heavy line. (You can spill out the water now.)

3. Measure off equal distances to the top of the bottle, also marking them with heavy lines on the paper strip. Then subdivide each section into ten equal parts. Remember, the large sections indicate inches and the subdivisions indicate tenths of inches *in terms of the can.*

4. To collect the rain, place the can outside in an open area where it will catch the rain from all directions. To prevent it from tipping in a strong wind, dig a hole several inches deep and set the can inside it. Empty the can each day.

5. Measure the amount of rainfall on a given day by pouring the rain water from the can through the funnel into the jar. Make your measurement as soon as the rain stops, to prevent loss of water through evaporation.

Observations

Your can, funnel, and jar will serve nicely as a simple rain gauge. In more elaborate gauges, however, the gathering and measuring devices are combined into one instrument.

■ FOG AND DEW

Purpose

Fog occurs when moist air is cooled at the surface of the earth by the ground or by the sea. Some of the water vapor condensing from the newly cooled air forms tiny drops which latch on to dust particles and float as a low-lying cloud. Dew occurs when air is cooled at night by the ground, and water vapor condenses on low-lying objects, such as leaves and grass and flowers. In the following experiments you will produce indoor versions of fog and dew.

Apparatus

milk bottle
cup of hot water
ice cubes
metal can

EXPERIMENT 1

Steps

1. Pour the cup of hot water into the bottle and set an ice cube in its mouth. Don't let the ice cube fall in.

2. Observe what happens on the inside of the bottle.

EXPERIMENT 2

Steps

1. Put several ice cubes inside the metal can, making sure that the outside is perfectly dry.

2. Observe what happens on the outside of the can.

Observations

In Experiment 1 the hot water makes the air inside the bottle warm and moist. The air rises, and is suddenly cooled by the ice. As the temperature falls, water condenses in light drops, making a swirling "fog" inside the bottle. In Experiment 2 the temperature of the outside air is lowered when it comes in contact with the surface of the colder ice-filled can. The water vapor in the air condenses, forming "dew" on the outside of the can.

■ FROST

Purpose

When below-freezing temperatures cool air close to the ground, moisture comes out of the air in a frozen state—as ice crystals—and frost appears on grass and windowpanes. Follow the instructions below and produce homemade frost.

Apparatus

ice cubes
3 tablespoons of salt
metal can

Steps

1. Fill the can with ice cubes.

2. Add the salt to the ice.

3. After a few minutes observe the outside of the can.

Observations

Frost forms on the outside of the can, because the temperature of the can is below freezing. The salt has lowered the melting point of the ice.

■ HUMIDITY

Purpose

Humidity is the amount of moisture (water vapor) dissolved in the air. Relative humidity (expressed as a per cent) is the amount of moisture the air is actually holding at a given temperature compared to the total amount of moisture it could hold at that same temperature. Relative humidity of 100% always means that the air is saturated—is holding all the moisture it can hold; relative humidity of 50% always means that the air contains half the amount of water it can hold, etc. Below are instructions for constructing a psychrometer—a device that measures relative humidity.

Apparatus

2 identical thermometers (Fahrenheit)
wooden board (A bread board is fine.)
2 rubber bands
wad of cotton
water

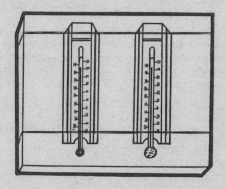

Steps

1. Moisten the wad of cotton thoroughly and pull it out until it is thin enough to be wrapped tightly around the entire bulb of one thermometer. There should be a free

circulation of air around the bulb. (If there is not, cut away the plastic or other material surrounding the bulb and let it hang freely.)

2. Place the thermometers side by side on the board. Allow a few inches between them. The bulbs should point toward the ground.

3. Hold the thermometers in place by wrapping the rubber bands over them and the board, one near the top, the other near the bottom. Stand the board outdoors where there is a free circulation of air, but avoid direct sunlight.

4. Fan the air around both bulbs for 3 or 4 minutes, until the temperature of the wet-bulb thermometer no longer drops. Then write down the temperature reading of each thermometer. Subtract the wet-bulb temperature from the dry-bulb temperature.

5. Turn to the Relative Humidity Table at the back of the book. By using the figures obtained in step 4, you can determine the relative humidity.

Observations

If there is a great difference between the amount of water vapor in the air and the amount it can hold, evaporation is rapid and much cooling occurs. Evaporation cools the wet-bulb thermometer, which registers a lower temperature than the dry. If there is a great difference between the readings of the two thermometers, the table shows a low relative humidity. If the air is holding almost all the water vapor it can hold, evaporation is slow and little cooling occurs. Thus the readings are almost the same and the table tells you the humidity is high.

WIND

■ WIND RATINGS

Purpose

Wind is moving air. It can be gentle or violent, depending on the speed with which it moves. You can rate winds from calm to hurricane by using a 12-point scale designed by an Admiral Beaufort. See the experiment below.

Apparatus

pencil and large piece of paper
ruler
observant eyes
common sense

SCALE NUMBER	WIND DESCRIPTION	WIND SPEED	WIND EFFECT
0	calm	under 1	
1	light air	1-3	
2	light breeze	4-7	

Steps

1. Divide the paper into four vertical columns. (Read the experiment through to determine how wide each column should be.)

2. Label across the top of each column as follows: scale number, wind description, wind speed, wind effect.

3. Number down the first column from 0 to 12.

4. Label down the second column as follows: calm, light air, light breeze, gentle breeze, moderate breeze, fresh wind, strong wind, high wind, gale, strong gale, whole gale, violent storm, hurricane.

5. Number down the third column as follows: under 1, 1–3, 4–7, 8–12, 13–18, 19–24, 25–31, 32–38, 39–46, 47–54, 55–63, 64–75, over 75.

6. Here are 13 wind descriptions. They are not in the proper order: (a) Trees are uprooted. (b) Drifting smoke shows wind direction. (c) Small trees sway. (d) Smoke rises vertically; flags are limp. (e) Leaves rustle; wind vanes turn. (f) It is hard to walk against the wind; whole trees sway. (g) Damage is widespread. (h) Flags blow straight out. (i) Destruction is widespread. (j) Branches break from trees; there is some slight damage to buildings. (k) It is extremely hard to walk against the wind; twigs break from trees. (l) Large branches move; outdoor telephone wires whistle. (m) Dust starts blowing. Can you list these descriptions correctly in the fourth column?

Observations

The list should appear in the following order: d, b, e, h, m, c, l, f, k, j, a, g, i. Your Beaufort Scale is now complete. Although it is not an exact scientific standard, it will be useful in giving you a rough estimate of wind speed.

■ THE ANEMOMETER

Purpose

The anemometer is a more precise tool for measuring wind speed. It is usually composed of three or four cups attached to horizontal arms set on a vertical shaft. The wind blows into the cups, making the arms turn, and a meter automatically clocks the speed in miles per hour. To make and use a simple version of the anemometer, do the following experiment.

Apparatus

8 pieces of cardboard, each 4 inches by 12 inches (Cut them from the cardboard that comes back with shirts from the laundry.)
stapler
scissors
ruler
4 paper cups, 3 white (or any color), 1 red (or any other color)
transparent tape
2 washers
small screw and screwdriver
wooden shaft, 12 inches long
clock with second hand

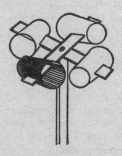

Steps

1. Place four pieces of cardboard in one pile, four pieces in another, one on top of the other.

2. Make an X by placing one pile between the strips of the other pile so that two strips are above and two are below.

3. Staple the strips together securely.

4. Attach the four cups to the four arms of the X so that all cup openings face in a counterclockwise direction. To do this, cut vertical slits in the front and back of each cup—wide enough to accommodate the arms—and push the arms through the slits. The cups should be about ½ inch from the outer ends.

5. Make a hole in the center of the X and use the tape to cover the rough edges around the hole.

6. The X should be attached horizontally to the vertical shaft as follows: place a washer on the screw, push the screw through the hole of the X, place the second washer below the X, and then screw the ensemble into the top of the shaft. The X must turn freely, but should not flop around.

7. Mount the anemometer where the wind can hit it from all directions. Count the number of times it turns in 30 seconds and divide by 5. (Every time the red cup passes, a turn is complete.) The resulting figure is the present wind speed in miles per hour.

Observations

For a more accurate reading from your anemometer, calibrate it in the following way. On a calm day sit in a car and hold the anemometer by its shaft out the front window. Have someone drive the car at a steady 5 mph. Count the number of times the anemometer turns at this speed within 30 seconds. Repeat at 10, 15, 20, 25 miles per hour. Make a chart of your findings.

■ THE WIND VANE

Purpose

The wind vane (also called a weather vane) points in the direction from which the wind is blowing. (It is this direction that gives the wind its name.) To construct a simple wind vane, follow the instructions below.

Apparatus

3 pieces of cardboard, one 4 inches by 8 inches, two 6 inches
   square
ruler
pencil
scissors
stapler
long thin nail
washer
hammer
wooden shaft, 12 inches long
compass

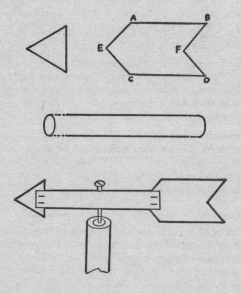

Steps

1. Roll the 8-inch-long piece of cardboard into a cylinder
and staple it in place. This will be the center section of your
vane.

2. Cut a pointer and a tail from the cardboard squares, using the illustrations as your models. The pointer should be
an equilateral triangle, 3 inches on each side. The tail
should measure 4 inches from A to B and C to D, 2 inches
from B to F and D to F, 2½ inches from A to E and C to E.

3. Make horizontal slits, about 1 inch long, at each end of the cylinder, top and bottom. (Make your cuts in the places indicated by dotted lines in the illustration.)

4. Put the pointer between the slits at one end, the tail between the slits at the other end, using the illustration as your model. Staple the pointer and tail in place.

5. Find the point along the cylinder at which the completed vane balances. Push the nail through the cylinder at this point and place the washer on the nail, beneath the cylinder.

6. Hammer the nail part way into the wooden shaft. Hold the shaft, and fan or blow the vane to be sure it moves freely around the nail.

7. Mount the vane where all the winds will strike it. Locate north with your compass so you can read your wind vane accurately.

Observations

Wind direction is often an indication of the weather. Keep a record of the winds and the weather they bring to your part of the country.

CLOUDS

■ **THE NEPHOSCOPE**

Purpose

Wind direction high in the sky is often different from wind direction close to earth. A good observer keeps records of both for a more complete picture of the weather. By watching the movements of clouds, you can determine in which direction the upper winds are blowing. To make your observations, build a useful cloud-gazing instrument called the nephoscope.

Apparatus

circular mirror, 4 to 6 inches in diameter
nail polish, or white paint
piece of cardboard, 8 to 10 inches square
compass
pencil
light, easy-to-move table

Steps

1. Put the mirror, reflecting side upward, in the center of the cardboard. Trace its outline with the pencil, to make certain you always return the mirror to the same place.

2. With the nail polish make a small dot in the center of the mirror.

3. Place the table outside, where the ground is perfectly level. Set the cardboard and mirror on top of the table.

4. Use the compass to locate north, then mark the compass points—N, NE, E, SE, S, SW, W, NW—all around the mirror on the cardboard.

5. To use your nephoscope, look into the mirror and watch for a cloud to cross the nail-polish dot. Follow this cloud until it passes from sight over the mirror's edge.

Observations

The point at which the cloud image drifts off the mirror (S, for example) is the direction *toward* which the wind is blowing. The point directly opposite (N) is the point *from* which the wind is blowing and for which the wind is named. In this example the upper wind is recorded as a north wind.

■ CLOUD TYPES

Purpose

Become acquainted with clouds by making models of the three basic types: cirrus, stratus and cumulus.

Apparatus

3 pieces of cardboard, 4 inches by 8 inches
box of cotton
glue
pen or pencil

Steps

1. Pull out some of the cotton to form long hairlike strands with curly ends. Glue them on a piece of cardboard in wisps curving upward across the sheet. Label this model *cirrus*.

2. Stretch some of the cotton into a solid horizontal line about ½ inch from top to bottom, about 5 inches from

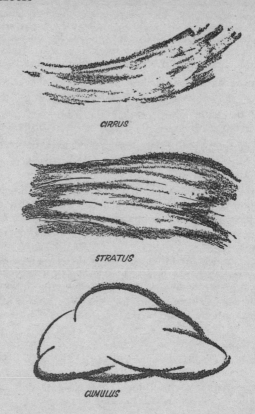

CIRRUS

STRATUS

CUMULUS

left to right. Repeat with three or four other pieces. Glue them on another piece of cardboard, one beneath the other, to give an appearance of a flat uniform layer. Label this model *stratus*.

3. Fluff up some of the cotton to make a fleecy heap with a rounded top and a flat base. Glue this model on the remaining piece of cardboard and label it *cumulus*.

Observations

Clouds are good signs of approaching weather. Cirrus clouds, very high in the sky, often foretell a coming storm. Stratus clouds may bring drizzle and gray skies. Cumulus clouds are fair-weather clouds, but can build up to thunderheads—

always a sign of rain. Scientists have subdivided these three cloud types into ten classifications: cirrus, cirrocumulus, cirrostratus, altocumulus, altostratus, nimbostratus, stratocumulus, stratus, cumulus, and cumulonimbus. (For more information on clouds, write to the U.S. Weather Bureau, Washington 25, D.C., and ask for its chart of Cloud Forms.)

TEMPERATURE

■ THE SLANT OF THE SUN'S RAYS

Purpose

Everyone knows that it is cold in the winter, hot in the summer, warm in the spring, and cool in the fall—all exceptions granted. One important explanation for changing seasons is that the sun's rays strike the earth at different angles at different times of the year. The less the sun's rays slant, the higher the temperature; the more they slant, the lower the temperature. The following experiments will show you why.

EXPERIMENT 1

Apparatus

flashlight
2 pieces of black paper
white chalk

Steps

1. Place a piece of the paper flat on a table, hold the flashlight slightly above it, and aim the beam directly down on it. Ask a friend to use the chalk to outline the spot of light on the black paper.

2. Repeat step 1 with the other piece of paper, this time holding the flashlight at an angle.

3. Compare the outlined spots of light in steps 1 and 2.

Observations

The spot of light is smaller in step 1, when the beam is direct, than in step 2, when the beam is at an angle. If the flashlight is the sun and the paper is the land, the land is getting a greater concentration of rays from the direct hit. Thus the temperature of the land is higher. The same number of rays, when spread out over a wider area, as in step 2, provide each segment of that area with less heat. Thus the temperature of the land is lower.

EXPERIMENT 2

Apparatus

drinking glass
water
ruler

Steps

1. Fill the glass with 4½ inches of water. (Measure the water level by standing the ruler next to the glass, on the outside.)

2. Now stand the ruler inside the glass, holding it perfectly straight. Remove the ruler and note that it is wet up to the 4½-inch mark.

3. Dry the ruler and put it back in the glass, this time at an angle. Is the water mark higher, lower, or the same as in step 2?

Observations

When the ruler is placed in the glass at an angle, it travels through more water than when it goes in straight. Thus the water mark is higher in step 3. In a similar way sun rays traveling to earth pass through more of the atmosphere when slanted than when straight. Since the atmosphere absorbs some of the radiant energy before it reaches the earth, more radiant energy is lost by the slanted rays, less heat reaches the ground, and the temperature is lower.

■ HEATING LAND AND SEA

EXPERIMENT 1

Purpose

In December the sun shines for about 9 hours a day; in July it shines for about 15 hours. The longer the sun shines, the warmer the weather, as the following experiment will show.

Apparatus

2 identical pans
2 identical thermometers
soil, enough to fill one pan
light, easy-to-move table

Steps

1. Bring the table outside on a sunny day and set the pans on top of it.

2. Divide the soil equally between the pans, and place a thermometer in each. (Don't allow the thermometers to touch bottom.)

3. After 15 minutes read the thermometers and record the temperatures. They should be identical.

4. Remove one pan and let the other remain for 15 minutes more. Now read the thermometer again and compare it with the readings in step 3.

Observations

The soil that remains in the sun for a total of 30 minutes has a higher temperature than the soil exposed for only 15 minutes. The temperature increases because the soil has a longer time to absorb the heat of the sun.

EXPERIMENT 2

Purpose

This experiment will demonstrate that the sun heats soil faster than it heats water. Soil, however, cools off more rapidly than water does.

Apparatus

2 identical pans
soil, enough to fill a pan
water, enough to fill a pan
light, easy-to-move table
refrigerator

Steps

1. Bring the table outside on a sunny day and set the pans on top of it.

2. Fill one pan with the soil, the other with the water, and let them sit in the sun for ½ hour.

3. Touch the top of the soil and the top of the water with your hand. You should easily be able to tell which is warmer.

4. Place the pans in the refrigerator for ½ hour, then repeat step 3.

Observations

The soil is warmer than the water in step 3, cooler than the water in step 4. Because the sun heats only the surface of the soil, the soil collects and loses heat more quickly than the water, which is warmed throughout.

■ FAHRENHEIT AND CENTIGRADE

Purpose

There are two widely used thermometer scales for measuring temperature—Fahrenheit and centigrade. Below, you will be introduced to these scales and will learn how to convert one to the other.

Apparatus

pencil and paper

EXPERIMENT 1

Steps

1. On the Fahrenheit scale, the boiling point of water is 212° and the freezing point is 32°. On the centigrade scale the boiling point is 100° and the freezing point is 0°. How many degrees does the Fahrenheit scale have? How many degrees does the centigrade scale have?

2. Using the figures obtained in step 1, determine the relationship between a centigrade degree and a Fahrenheit degree.

Observations

There are 180 degrees on the F. scale (212 minus 32). There are 100 degrees on the C. scale (100 minus 0). A Fahrenheit degree is ⅝ (that is, $^{100}/_{180}$) of a centigrade degree. A centigrade degree is ⅘ (that is, $^{180}/_{100}$) of a Fahrenheit degree.

Experiment 2

Steps

1. When a thermometer registers 77° F., it is 25° C. Can you convert 122° F. to centigrade?

2. When a thermometer registers 5° C., it is 41° F. Can you convert 40° C. to Fahrenheit?

Observations

We converted 77° F. to 25° C. as follows:

$77 - 32 = 45$; $45 \times \frac{5}{9} = 25$.

We converted 5° C. to 41° F. as follows:

$5 \times \frac{9}{5} = 9$; $9 + 32 = 41$.

If you used this method to make the conversions in steps 1 and 2, your answers will be 122° F. = 50° C. and 40°C. = 104° F.

PART 5
NUMBERS

The story of numbers probably began with the first man who recognized that he had more fingers than eyes, and more teeth than fingers. Between then and now, people have learned to add four sticks to five sticks, subtract one goat from three goats, multiply width by length, and divide Gaul into three parts. They have also learned—quite recently—to turn over many lengthy and complex number problems to electronic computers, which can find the answers faster than mathematicians can ask the questions.

The experiments in this section include a variety of number problems: some not-so-easy arithmetic, some not-so-difficult algebra and geometry, some ways to measure length and weight. The apparatus required for these experiments is often very simple: If you have one clear head, you are ready to begin.

■ THINKING WITH NUMBERS

Purpose

Here are some warming-up exercises to get you into the swing of thinking with numbers. See how many of these old problems you can solve.

Apparatus

pencil and paper
clear head

Problems

1. If a vase and a flower cost $1.10, and the vase costs $1 more than the flower, what is the price of each?

2. Two banks offered Milton a job. Both said they would start him at a salary of $350 a month. The National Bank said it would give him a $5 raise every six months. The Federal Bank said it would give him a $10 raise every year. In which job would he make more money? Or are the offers the same?

3. A snail is trying to climb out of a 10-foot well. He crawls up 3 feet each day and slides back 2 feet each night. How long will it take him to climb out of the well?

4. There are 6 pairs of gray socks and 6 pairs of green socks in the dresser drawer. If you went to the drawer blindfolded, how many socks would you have to take out to be sure of having a pair?

5. If 6 boys eat 6 sandwiches in 6 minutes, how many boys are needed to eat 100 sandwiches in 100 minutes?

Observations

If you couldn't solve the above problems, here are the answers. Can you figure out how we got them? 1. The vase costs $1.05; the flower costs $ .05. 2. The National Bank is offering more money. 3. Eight days. 4. Three socks. 5. Six boys.

■ ADDITION-SUBTRACTION SLIDE RULE

Purpose

Various gadgets have been invented to make computation less difficult and more accurate. This experiment will show

you how to construct and use a simple computing device—
an addition-subtraction slide rule.

Apparatus

piece of white paper, 11 inches by 1⅝ inches
piece of thick cardboard, 11 inches by 3⅝ inches
scissors, razor, or knife
glue
ruler
pencil

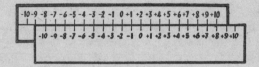

Steps

First prepare the slide rule:

1. Hold the white paper with its 11-inch sides horizontal.
Draw a line (let's call it x) from left to right, ⅝ inches down
from the upper edge.

2. Draw 21 parallel lines, ½ inch long and ½ inch apart,
bisected perpendicularly by line x. The eleventh line should
be in the exact center of x.

3. At the top of each parallel line number as follows:
—10, —9, —8, —7, —6, —5, —4, —3, —2, —1, 0, +1, +2,
+3, +4, +5, +6, +7, +8, +9, +10. Do the same at the bottom of the lines.

4. Cut along line x. You now have two scales with identical
markings.

5. From the cardboard cut three strips each 1 by 11 inches,
and a fourth strip ⅝ by 11 inches. Be sure your measurements are exact, and don't bend the cardboard.

6. Make a sandwich of three of the cardboard strips, placing
the narrow strip between two wide ones. Line up one side
of the three strips and glue securely together. Don't paste
the top of the two wide strips to each other—they must stand
apart to provide a slot through which the fourth strip can
slide.

7. You now have the base of your addition-subtraction slide rule. To complete it, smoothly glue the wide scale along one length of it.

8. To the upper part of the fourth strip paste the narrow scale. Be sure that the numbers of the sliding scale and the base are aligned perfectly when the sliding scale is in the slot. Also make sure that the strip slides easily through the slot.

Now you are ready to add and subtract with your rule.

9. The zero point on each scale is called the index. To add +6 and +3, put the index of the sliding scale over the +6 on the base. Locate +3 on the sliding scale, and you will find your answer directly under it.

10. Try adding a negative number (−5) to a positive number (+2). Place the top index over +2, locate −5 on the sliding scale, and read the answer directly under it, on the base.

11. To subtract +4 from +9, line up the +4 on your sliding scale with the +9 on the base. You'll find your answer beneath the index of the sliding scale.

12. Your addition-subtraction slide rule will also subtract two negative numbers. To subtract −1 from −8, place the −1 of the sliding scale above the −8 of the base, and look under the top index for your answer.

Observations

The numbers on your addition-subtraction slide rule represent distances, with the index as your constant starting point. It is a helpful fact to keep in mind when using this computing device. You might also want to be reminded of the rule for subtraction: change the sign of the number being subtracted—and add.

■ HOW DO YOU WRITE . . . ?

Purpose

How do you write the number 3, using four 5's? It's easy, if you do it like this— $\frac{5 + 5 + 5}{5}$. With only the addition, subtraction, multiplication, and division signs, and the numbers given below, see if you can do the following problems.

Apparatus

pencil and paper
clear head

Problems

1. How do you write 0, using two 7's?
2. How do you write 30, using three 6's?
3. How do you write 8, using four 4's?
4. How do you write 1, using four 3's?
5. How do you write 9, using three 8's?
6. How do you write 720, using four 9's?
7. How do you write ½, using four 2's?
8. How do you write ⅓, using four 1's?
9. How do you write 4, using four 5's?
10. How do you write 3, using four 10's?

Observations

Here are our answers: (1) $7 - 7$; (2) $(6 \times 6) - 6$; (3) $4 + \dfrac{4 \times 4}{4}$;

(4) $3 - \dfrac{3 + 3}{3}$; (5) $\dfrac{8}{8} + 8$; (6) $(9 \times 9 \times 9) - 9$; (7) $\dfrac{2 - \dfrac{2}{2}}{2}$;

(8) $\dfrac{1}{1 + 1 + 1}$; (9) $\dfrac{(5 \times 5) - 5}{5}$; (10) $\dfrac{10 + 10 + 10}{10}$.

■ MAGIC SQUARES

Purpose

In a magic square, the sum of each horizontal column, each vertical column and the two diagonals is the same. The square is made up of the numbers 1, 2, 3 . . . , one number used for each division on the square, no number used more than once. See if you can discover the pattern in magic squares and make a square of your own.

Apparatus

pencil and paper
clear head

EXPERIMENT 1

Steps

1. Draw a square divided into three rows of three squares each.

2. In the first row fill in the left square with the number 4, the middle square with number 9.

3. In the second row fill in the middle square with number 5, the right square with number 7.

4. In the third row fill in the left square with number 8.

5. Now fill in the blanks to make a magic square, using up the rest of the numbers between 1 and 9.

Observations

Each column and diagonal will add up to 15.

EXPERIMENT 2

Steps

1. Draw a square divided into four rows of four squares each.

2. Fill in number 5 in the second from left square, row 1. In the same row fill in number 4 in the right square.

3. Fill in number 11 in the left square, row 2.

4. Fill in number 10 in the right square, row 3.

5. Fill in number 8 in the second from right square, row 4.

6. Using the rest of the numbers from 1 to 16, and never using a number more than once, make a magic square.

Observations

Here is a hint if you need one. Each column and diagonal will add up to 34.

Steps

1. Draw a square divided into five rows of five squares each.

2. Using the numbers 1 to 25, make your own magic square.

Observations

In working out these squares, we first determined what each column and diagonal should add up to. For the 3-by-3 square we added 1 through 9 and divided by 3 to get 15. For the 4-by-4 square we added 1 through 16 and divided by 4 to get 34.

■ COMPUTER ARITHMETIC

Purpose

All the numbers in our numerical system can be expressed by ten symbols—nine digits and a zero. But a number system based on ten is just one of many possibilities. Computers use a system based on two, called the binary system, which involves only the symbols 0 and 1. All numbers can be expressed by these two symbols. The following experiments will introduce you to binary numbers.

Apparatus

pencil and paper

Steps

1. Write the symbols 11111 on a piece of paper, Reading from right to left, this is what they represent: The first column represents 2^0, which is 1. The second column represents 2^1, which is 2. The third column represents 2^2, which is 4. The fourth column represents 2^3, which is 8. The fifth column represents 2^4, which is 16. Add $1 + 2 + 4 + 8 + 16$, and your result will be the number represented by the binary symbols 11111.

2. The symbol 1 indicates the presence of a power of two. The location of the 1 tells which power of two is present. If a power of two is not present, the symbol 0 appears in the proper place. Write 10010. Read from right to left. There is no power of two in the first column. The second column represents 2. There is no power of two in the third column,

or in the fourth. In the fifth column 16 is represented. Thus 10010 stands for the number $2 + 16$, which is 18.

3. In the binary system the numbers 1, 2, 3, 4, and 5 are written 1, 10, 11, 100, 101. Study steps 1 and 2 and see if you can understand why. Now write the numbers 6 to 10 in binary.

4. Remember that any number can be written in the binary system. What does 101101110 represent?

5. To prove that you understand binary numbers, write 533 in binary.

Observations

Here are the answers to 3, 4, and 5. In binary the numbers 6 to 10 are written 110, 111, 1000, 1001 and 1010. The binary number 101101110 represents 366. (Remember how we got this? There is no 2^0. There is a 2^1, which is 2; a 2^2, which is 4; a 2^3, which is 8. There is no 2^4. There is a 2^5, which is 32; and a 2^6, which is 64. There is no 2^7. There is a 2^8, which is 256. Add up the powers that are represented, and you will have 366.) Step 5 asks you to write 533 using only 1's and 0's. This number written in binary is 1000010101.

EXPERIMENT 2

Steps

1. Make two columns on a piece of paper. Put the number 85 in the left column and the number 37 in the right. We are going to show you an odd-looking method of multiplying these two numbers together, based on the binary system.

2. Divide 85 by 2. Your result will be 42½. Ignore the fraction and list 42 under 85. Divide 42 by 2 and list your result. Continue dividing (always ignoring the fractions) and list your results until you have reached 1. Your left column will look like this:

$$85$$
$$42 \text{ (ignore the fraction)}$$
$$21$$
$$10 \text{ (ignore the fraction)}$$
$$5$$
$$2 \text{ (ignore the fraction)}$$
$$1$$

3. Now go to work on the right column. Multiply 37 by 2 and list the result (74) under the 37. Multiply 74 by 2 and

list. Continue until you have multiplied by 2 as many times as you divided by 2 in the left column. The two columns together look like this:

85	37
42	74
21	148
10	296
5	592
2	1184
1	2368

4. Cross off all the even numbers in the left column (42, 10, and 2) and all the corresponding numbers in the right column (74, 296, and 1184). Forget about the left column and add up the remaining numbers in the right column. These will be:

37
148
592
2368

5. Multiply 85 by 37 the regular way and compare it with your answer in 4. They should be identical.

6. This system, sometimes called peasant multiplication, can be used to multiply any two sets of numbers. Try it out on any numbers you wish and test your results by multiplying the same numbers in the conventional way.

Observations

The reason why peasant multiplication works can be explained by the binary system. Let's go back to 85 times 37. What you are actually doing is changing 85 to binary form, multiplying each power of two that is present by 37 and adding the results. You convert 85 to a binary number by dividing down by 2. When your result is an odd number, place a 1 beside it. When your result is an even number, place a 0 beside it. Thus:

85	1
42	0
21	1
10	0
5	1
2	0
1	1

Reading from bottom to top you have the binary representation of 85—1010101. Now multiply 37 by each of the powers that are present:

$$2^0 \text{ times } 37 \text{ is } \quad 37$$
$$\text{there is no } 2^1$$
$$2^2 \text{ times } 37 \text{ is } \quad 148$$
$$\text{there is no } 2^3$$
$$2^4 \text{ times } 37 \text{ is } \quad 592$$
$$\text{there is no } 2^5$$
$$2^6 \text{ times } 37 \text{ is } 2368$$

Now total the products. $\quad$ 3145

ALGEBRA

■ ALGEBRA WHEELS

Purpose

Spin a pointer and see where it stops on a numbered cardboard disk. Spin it again, and another pair of numbers will come up. Build four simple algebra wheels, set the pointers spinning, and work out the equations for which each wheel was designed.

Apparatus

4 pieces of cardboard, about 6 inches square
4 drinking straws
4 thumbtacks
compass
pencil
scissors

EXPERIMENT 1

Steps

1. Use your compass to make a circle 6 inches in diameter on a piece of cardboard. Cut it out.

2. Make another circle, 5 inches in diameter, within the first circle. Do not cut.

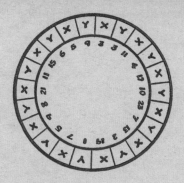

3. In the space between the two circumferences mark off 22 equal divisions. Label the first *x*, the second *y*, the third *x*, etc., alternating *x*'s and *y*'s all around the wheel.

4. Just inside the inner circumference, mark off numbers all around the wheel. The first number should go directly under an *x* (any *x*) and the numbers follow clockwise in the order given here:

x	*y*	*x*	*y*	*x*	*y*	*x*	*y*	*x*	*y*	*x*	*y*
3	3	11	4	17	10	23	7	13	2	19	1

x	*y*	*x*	*y*	*x*	*y*	*x*	*y*	*x*	*y*
7	5	9	8	21	11	15	6	5	9

5. Cut one of the straws to 4 inches in length. Push a tack through the middle of it and attach it to the center of the wheel. It should spin easily.

6. If you have marked your wheel correctly, the spins of the pointer will show the following combinations:

when *x* is: 7 11 9 17 21 23 15 13 5 19 3
      y is: 3 5 4 8 10 11 7 6 2 9 1

7. What does *x* equal in terms of *y*?

EXPERIMENTS 2, 3, AND 4

Steps

1. Follow steps 1, 2, and 3 of Experiment 1, using the three remaining pieces of cardboard to make your wheels.

2. Mark off numbers as described in step 4 of Experiment 1, but use the following three combinations:

Wheel 2:

x	y	x	y	x	y	x	y	x	y	x	y
2	7	6	3	4	9	10	14	3	10	9	4

x	y	x	y	x	y	x	y	x	y
5	8	1	6	7	12	12	5	8	11

Wheel 3:

x	y	x	y	x	y	x	y	x	y	x	y
7	6	16	9	37	2	13	5	28	7	34	1

x	y	x	y	x	y	x	y	x	y
22	4	31	11	10	3	19	8	25	10

Wheel 4:

x	y	x	y	x	y	x	y	x	y	x	y
4	7	7½	6	6	12	2½	3	4½	2	6½	4

x	y	x	y	x	y	x	y	x	y
5½	11	5	8	8	1	3½	5	3	9

3. Attach straw pointers as directed in step 5 of Experiment 1.

4. What does x equal for Wheel 2, for Wheel 3, for Wheel 4?

Observations

The answer to x will always be in terms of y. After you have worked out the four answers, check with these:

Wheel 1: $x = 2y + 1$
Wheel 2: $x = y - 2$
Wheel 3: $x = 3y + 4$
Wheel 4: $x = \dfrac{y + 4}{2}$

You can devise other algebra wheels (with less than 22 numbers if you're lazy). Try a 16-number wheel for the equation $x = 5y - 8$. Try an 18-number wheel for the equation $x = \dfrac{2y + 3}{4}$. Work out your own equations, make wheels for them and try them on your friends.

■ THINK OF A NUMBER

Purpose

Think of a Number is an old game in which player 1 picks a number and then adds, subtracts, multiplies, and divides as directed by player 2. At the end of all this arithmetic—without knowing the initial number—player 2 can astound player 1 by telling him the number he has ended up with. This is not done with a crystal ball, but with algebra. For, as the following problems will show, a meaningful relationship among a group of numbers can be written as an algebraic equation.

Apparatus

pencil and paper
clear head

EXPERIMENT 1

Steps

1. Think of a number.
2. Double it.
3. Add 10.
4. Divide by 2.
5. Subtract the number you started with.

Observations

No matter what number you started with, your answer is 5. The equation for this problem is $\dfrac{2x + 10}{2} - x = 5$.

EXPERIMENT 2

Steps

1. Think of a number.
2. Multiply by 4.
3. Add 18.
4. Divide by 2.
5. Subtract 7.
6. Multiply by 3.

7. Divide by 6.

8. Subtract the number you started with.

9. Your answer is 1. Can you work out the equation?

Observations

The equation for this problem is $\dfrac{3\left(\dfrac{4x+18}{2}-7\right)}{6}-x=1$

EXPERIMENT 3

Steps

1. Think of a number.

2. Triple it.

3. Add 21.

4. Subtract 9.

5. Divide by 3.

6. Multiply by 4.

7. Divide by 8.

8. Subtract half the number you started with.

9. Your answer is 2. Can you work out the equation?

Observations

The equation for this problem is $\dfrac{4\left(\dfrac{3x+21-9}{3}\right)}{8}-\tfrac{1}{2}x=2.$

EXPERIMENT 4

Note: Here is a variation on Think of a Number involving two unknowns.

Steps

1. Take your age (10 or over).

2. Double it.

3. Subtract 5.

4. Multiply by 50.

5. Add 265.

6. Add any number from 10 to 99.

7. Subtract 15.

8. You now have a four digit number. The first two digits will be your age; the last two will be the number from 10 to 99 that you added in step 6. Using x for the first unknown and y for the second, see if you can work out the equation for this problem.

Observations

The equation is $50 (2x - 5) + 265 + y - 15 = 100x + y$.

■ ALGEBRA PUZZLES

Purpose

Here are five puzzles, each requiring the use of more than one equation for its solution. You may be tempted to guess at the answers, and perhaps you'll come up with the correct ones. But we recommend solving these puzzles the algebra way—it's more fun.

Apparatus

paper and pencil
clear head

Problems

1. Both of us have some books. Give me one of yours and then I'll have twice as many as you'll have. Or take one of mine and then we'll both have the same amount. How many books do you have? How many books have I?

2. Here is a basket of apples and bananas. If I buy three more apples and eat five bananas, there will be an equal amount of each fruit in the basket. Or if I double the number of apples I have now, I'll have three more apples than bananas. How many apples and bananas do I have?

3. Three cats are sunning themselves on the window sill. Daphne weighs twice as much as Alison, plus ½ pound. Pere weighs 1¾ pounds less than Alison, and is only ⅓ the size of Daphne. What does each cat weigh?

4. Julie's age is Danny's age minus Polly's. Katie is 4 years younger than Julie. Polly is 3 times as old as Katie and 2 years older than Julie. How old are Danny, Polly, Katie, and Julie?

5. If B is 6 times A, and C is ½ B; if D is 3 more than E and 13 less than G; if F is B plus D, and also G minus D; if A is $\frac{1}{20}$ G, what are A, B, C, D, E, F, G?

Observations

By putting the given information in terms of algebraic equations, you can find the answers to these puzzles. You can make sure your answers are correct by going back to the puzzles and testing them out. Here is how we did them:

1. Call my books x and your books y.

$x + 1$ (my books plus one of yours) $= 2(y - 1)$

(twice your books less the one you gave to me)

$x - 1$ (my books less one I gave to you) $= y + 1$

(your books plus one of mine)

if $x - 1 = y + 1$, then $x = y + 2$

if $x + 1 = 2(y - 1)$, then $x + 1 = 2y - 2$

$$y + 2 + 1 = 2y - 2$$
$$y + 3 = 2y - 2$$

therefore: $y = 5 \qquad x = 7$

2. Call apples a, and bananas b.

given: $a + 3 = b - 5 \qquad 2a = b + 3$

therefore: $a = b - 8 \qquad 2(b - 8) = b + 3 \qquad 2b - 16 = b + 3$

$b = 19 \qquad a = 11$

3. Call Daphne d, Alison a, Pere p.

given: $d = 2a + \frac{1}{2} \qquad p = a - 1\frac{3}{4} \qquad p = \frac{1}{3} d$

therefore: $d = 3p \qquad 3p = 2a + \frac{1}{2} \qquad 3(a - 1\frac{3}{4}) = 2a + \frac{1}{2}$

$3a - 5\frac{1}{4} = 2a + \frac{1}{2} \qquad a = 5\frac{3}{4} \qquad p = 4 \qquad d = 12$

4. Call Danny d, Julie j, Polly p, Katie k.

given: $j = d - p \qquad k = j - 4 \qquad p = 3k \qquad p = j + 2$

therefore: $3k = j + 2 \qquad k = \dfrac{j + 2}{3} \qquad \dfrac{j + 2}{3} = j - 4$

$j + 2 = 3j - 12 \qquad 2j = 14 \qquad j = 7 \qquad k = 3$

$p = 9 \qquad d = 16$

5. given: $B = 6A \qquad C = \frac{1}{2}B \qquad D = E + 3 \qquad D = G - 13$

$F = B + D \qquad F = G - D \qquad A = \frac{1}{20}G$ or $G = 20A$

therefore: $D = 20A - 13 \qquad F = 20A - (20A - 13) \qquad F = 13$

$B + D = 13 \qquad 6A + 20A - 13 = 13 \qquad 26A = 26$

$A = 1 \quad B = 6 \quad C = 3 \quad D = 7 \quad E = 4 \quad G = 20$

■ FIGURES OF GEOMETRY

Purpose

Can you identify the figures of geometry? We'll tell you how to construct eight shapes and we'll give you eight names. See if you are able to match them up.

Apparatus

pencil and paper
protractor
ruler
compass

Steps

First make the figures.

1. Construct a figure with all sides equal.

2. Construct a parallelogram with four equal sides.

3. Construct a triangle with two equal sides.

4. Construct a five-sided figure.

5. Construct a parallelogram with four right angles.

6. Construct a triangle with no equal sides.

7. Construct a four-sided figure with one set of parallel sides.

8. Construct a figure which at every point is the same distance from its center.

Now match the figures with these names.

9. isosceles triangle

10. rectangle

11. trapezoid

12. equilateral polygon

13. circle

14. scalene triangle

15. pentagon

16. rhombus

Observations

Here are the correct combinations: 1 and 12; 2 and 16; 3 and 9; 4 and 15; 5 and 10; 6 and 14; 7 and 11; 8 and 13.

■ THE CIRCLE

Purpose

It is said that there are no perfect circles in nature; they are man's own invention. The experiments below will show you how to construct original circles and will demonstrate some interesting facts about this fundamental geometric form.

Apparatus

2 pieces of red paper, 7 inches square
2 pieces of blue paper, 7 inches square
2 pieces of yellow paper, 7 inches square
drawing board
tack
straight pin
piece of string, about 8 inches long
pencil
scissors
ruler
compass
protractor

Experiment 1

Steps

1. Tack a piece of the red paper (in its center) to the drawing board.

2. Hook one end of the string around the tack; tie the other end to the pencil. When the string is attached, its length from tack to pencil should be no more than 3 inches.

3. Holding the string taut, let the pencil rotate around the tack. When the pencil returns to its starting point, you will have a perfect circle.

4. Using the same technique, make a circle on the other piece of red paper. It should be identical to the first.

5. Snip ½ inch from the string and make two identical circles on the blue papers.

6. Snip another ½ inch from the string and make two identical circles on the yellow papers.

7. Cut out your six original circles.

EXPERIMENT 2

Steps

1. Fold a red circle in half, then in quarters. Unfold. Push the straight pin through the point where the folds intersect. This is the center of your circle.

2. Fold down the second red circle so that a chord is formed. Fold down another part of the circle and make a second chord. Bisect each chord with a perpendicular line and push the straight pin through the point where these lines intersect.

3. Place the second circle on top of the first so that the pin holes match. You will find that the second circle covers the first circle completely.

4. What do you conclude about the position of the hole in the second circle?

EXPERIMENT 3

Steps

1. Fold a blue circle in half and cut, making two semicircles.

2. Label the diameter of the first semicircle AB.

3. Fold a chord that is connected at one end to A. Label its other end C.

4. Connect B and C.

5. Repeat the same procedure on the other semicircle, but make the chord AC shorter or longer than the chord in the first semicircle.

6. Use a yellow circle to inscribe two other angles in semicircles, again varying the length of chord AC.

7. Measure the angle ACB in each semicircle. Does the length of the chord change the size of the angle? Does the size of the circle change the size of the angle?

EXPERIMENT 4

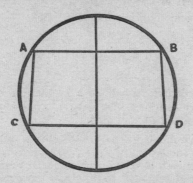

Steps

1. Fold a yellow circle in half to make a diameter. Unfold.

2. Fold two lines, AB and CD, perpendicular to the diameter, thus forming two parallel chords.

3. Fold a chord AC; fold a chord BD.

4. Cut out the four-sided figure you have formed and measure AC against BD.

5. Repeat steps 1 and 2 with the remaining blue circle, but make the lines AB and CD longer or shorter. Repeat steps 3 and 4.

6. What is the relationship of AB to CD?

Observations

Make larger circles, smaller circles, orange circles, purple circles, and try these experiments. You will find that the geometric laws which they demonstrate are constant, no matter the size of the circle. Perpendicular lines bisecting chords will always intercept at a circle's center; the only angle you can inscribe in a semicircle is a 90° angle; the lines that connect parallel chords will always be equal.

■ THE TRIHEXAFLEXAGON

Problems

A hexagon is a six-sided figure. A regular hexagon is a figure whose six sides and six angles are equal. Six equilateral triangles make up a regular hexagon, but 18 equilaterals are displayed by the trihexaflexagon, a geometric structure that has the ability to flex in most interesting ways. Below are instructions for constructing and operating a trihexaflexagon.

Apparatus

strip of paper, 2½ inches wide and 20 or more inches long
compass
protractor
ruler
blue crayon
red crayon
glue
scissors

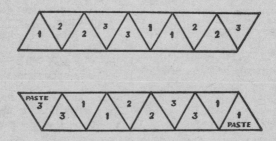

Steps

First construct your trihexaflexagon.

1. Make an equilateral triangle on the paper strip, close to the left end. The lower edge of the strip should form the base of the triangle, and the apex should be a point on the upper edge. Call the points that form the base x and y; call the apex z. Cut off the excess paper to the left of the triangle only.

2. Make a second equilateral triangle by folding along line yz and bringing point x to the upper edge of the strip. (The apex of this triangle will be on the lower edge.) Use this technique to make a chain of ten triangles along the strip. Cut off the excess paper to the right of your final triangle.

3. Reverse all the creases between the triangles to keep your flexagon flexible.

4. Lay the triangle chain flat on a table. The front side should be numbered in the center of each triangle and lettered in the angles of the triangles as follows:

	number	letter
first triangle (apex up)	1	*a*—lower right angle
second triangle	2	*a*—apex angle
third triangle	2	*a*—lower left angle
		d—lower right angle
fourth triangle	3	*d*—apex angle
fifth triangle	3	*d*—lower left angle
		g—lower right angle
sixth triangle	1	*b*—apex angle
		c—upper right angle
seventh triangle	1	*c*—apex angle
		b—lower left angle
eighth triangle	2	*e*—apex angle
		c—upper left angle
		f—upper right angle
ninth triangle	2	*f*—apex angle
		e—lower left angle
tenth triangle	3	*h*—apex angle
		f—upper left angle
		a—upper right angle

5. Turn the chain on its unmarked side, so that the first triangle is the same as in step 4, except that its apex is pointing down. Number and letter the back of the chain as follows:

	number	letter
first triangle (apex down)	3	none
second triangle	3	*a*—apex angle
		h—lower left angle
third triangle	1	*a*—upper left angle
		d—upper right angle
fourth triangle	1	*d*—apex angle
fifth triangle	2	*d*—upper left angle
		g—upper right angle
sixth triangle	2	*g*—apex angle
		c—lower right angle
seventh triangle	3	*g*—upper left angle
eighth triangle	3	*f*—lower right angle
ninth triangle	1	none
tenth triangle	1	none

6. Fold each pair of adjacent 2's together, face to face. You now have a hexagon with triangles labeled 1 appearing on one side and triangles labeled 3 appearing on the other.

The tenth triangle overlaps the first and should be pasted to it. (Be sure to paste together the *unlettered* sides.)

7. Lightly color the triangles labeled 1 with your blue crayon. Lightly color the triangles labeled 3 with your red crayon.

Now you are ready to operate your trihexaflexagon:

8. Hold the trihexaflexagon with the blue face on top. Fold the blue corner labeled *aa*, bringing together the back red triangles also labeled *aa*. Push in the blue corner labelled *bb* and pull out the blue corner labeled *cc*. The hexagon will open up flat with its white face, labeled 2 on every triangle, on top. The process of opening the flexagon to show a new face is called a flexion.

9. Fold the white corner *dd*, bringing together the back blue triangles also labeled *dd*. Push in the white corner *ee* and pull out the white corner *ff*. The flexagon will open up flat with its red face showing.

10. To turn up the blue face again, fold the red *gg*, bringing together the white *gg*. Push in the red *hh* and pull out the red *aa*.

Observations

There are other ways to make the trihexaflexagon show its three faces. Experiment by flexing it at other corners. You will find that sometimes the flexagon won't open on top—this means that the flexion is blocked. But don't give up. Try another corner; you will find an unblocked flexion and you can keep flexing your trihexaflexagon indefinitely.

■ THE MOEBIUS STRIP

Purpose

When does a strip of paper have only one edge and one surface? You can see for yourself, by making a Moebius strip. To pronounce the word, by the way, say *mur-bius,* but go easy on the *r.*

Apparatus

strip of paper, 1 inch wide and 1 foot long
glue
crayon
scissors

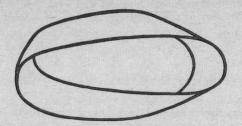

Steps

1. Hold the strip in your hand and study it. You will find it to be a perfectly ordinary strip, with a front and a back.

2. Give the strip a half twist and glue the ends together. You now have a Moebius strip, which is not an ordinary strip at all.

3. Place the crayon at any point on the edge of the strip and run it along the edge until you come back to where you started. You will find that no part of the edge remains uncrayoned.

4. Place the crayon at any point on the surface of the strip and draw a line lengthwise until you return to your starting point. No part of the surface will remain unmarked.

5. Cut lengthwise down the center of your Moebius strip. When you return to your starting point you will have in your hand *one* strip still. It will be double the length and half the width of the original.

Observations

The Moebius strip study belongs to a special branch of geometry called topology, which studies the properties of geometrical figures that do not change, even when the figures are twisted, stretched, or otherwise deformed without tearing. In the world of topology, yesterday's square is today's circle, and distances are not to be counted on. You can't even trust a Moebius strip, in fact. Try cutting lengthwise down the center of a strip after giving it a *full* twist. Can you predict the result?

MEASUREMENT

■ **MEASURING WITH TRIANGLES**

Purpose

The following three problems in measurement can be solved without any measuring whatsoever, if you know a few simple facts about triangles. See if you can find the answers, using only pencil and paper.

Apparatus

pencil and paper
ruler—just for checking answers
protractor—just for checking answers

Problems

1. Jody is standing 4 feet from the base of a 9-foot wall that is perpendicular to the ground. She is staring at a point ⅔ from the top of the wall. What is the distance from that point to the place where she is standing?

2. My house is 8½ feet from a birdbath, which is an unknown distance from an apple tree. The house (H), bath (B) and tree (T) form a triangle whose angle HBT measures 74°. The angle BTH is 53°. What is the distance from the birdbath to the apple tree?

3. A flagpole stands at an equal distance from a hotel and a museum. The three points form a triangle whose angle HFM is 60°. If half the distance from hotel to museum is 1½ miles, how far is the flagpole from the two buildings?

Observations

If you can't solve these problems, go back and try again, keeping in mind that (a) in a right triangle the square on the hypotenuse equals the sum of the squares on the other two sides; (b) the sum of a triangle's angles must always be 180°; (c) a triangle with three equal angles must have three equal sides; (d) if a triangle has two equal angles, the sides opposite these angles must also be equal. If you think you have the correct answers now, use your ruler and protractor to draw the triangles and check their measurements.

■ MEASURING OFF A LINE

Purpose

Suppose you have a line which is 4⅞ inches long. Suppose you must divide this line into 19 equal parts. Now it is much easier to divide a 19-inch line or a 9½-inch line into 19 equal parts than it is to grapple with a line of 4⅞ inches. Here is how you can arrive at the difficult measurement by doing the easy one.

Apparatus

pencil and paper
ruler
protractor

Steps

1. Use the ruler to draw your 4⅞-inch line. Call it XY.

2. At any angle to XY draw a line XZ. Make it 19 inches long, or 9½ inches long.

3. You can easily measure off 19 equal parts on XZ. If you are using the 19-inch line, simply place your ruler along XZ and put a dot at each inch mark. For the 9½-inch line put a dot at each ½-inch point.

4. Connect point Z (your final division mark) to point Y.

5. Now draw lines from each marked-off point on line XZ to the undivided XY. Make the lines parallel to YZ.

6. The points at which your parallel lines cross line XY will divide XY into 19 equal parts. You can verify this with your ruler.

Observations

Any line can be measured off into any number of equal divisions by this same method. If parallel lines cut off equal segments of one line, they will cut off equal segments of another.

■ MEASURING WEIGHT

Purpose

Weighing by balancing probably goes back to cave-dweller days, when a man first decided which of two stones was heavier by hefting one in each hand. Since that time a variety of balances have been devised. The experiments below will show you how to construct three weighing devices based on balance—a simple beam balance, a length-weight balance, and a spring balance.

EXPERIMENT 1

Apparatus

2 soda straws
3 straight pins
3 pieces of string, 2 equal in length, 1 longer
2 paper cups
salt
ruler
pencil

Steps

1. Measure in ¼ inch from each end of each straw. Mark these points with an X.

2. Find the point midway between the X's and mark this point Y on each straw.

3. Connect the straws side by side by inserting straight pins through each set of points X and through points Y. Separate the straws ¼ inch.

4. Tie the longer string to the center pin and suspend your balance by the other end of the string from a table or shelf edge. The straws should hang level. If they tilt at one end, adjust the pins until you achieve a perfect balance.

5. Attach the equal pieces of string to the paper cups and hang one from each end pin. Adjust your balance again if necessary until the cups are in equilibrium.

6. Pour salt in each cup until the cups are balanced. The cups of salt are equal in weight.

7. Pour ½ ounce of salt in one cup and add salt to the other until the cups are balanced.

Observations

The beam balance you have constructed can show whether materials are equal in weight. If they are not, you can learn which is the heavier material simply by looking at the balance. If you add a known weight to one of the cups, you can measure out an equal weight of a material in the other.

EXPERIMENT 2

Apparatus
12-inch ruler
3 pieces of thread, 2 equal in length, 1 longer
box of paper clips
drill
knife

Steps

1. Drill a hole at the 6-inch mark of the ruler, close to the upper edge.

2. Make notches above all the inch marks on the ruler, except the 6 and the 12.

3. Tie the longer thread through the hole and suspend the ruler from a shelf or table edge.

4. Tie the shorter threads into equal loops and loop one over the 1-inch notch, the other over the 11-inch notch.

5. Hang two paper clips from each loop. The ruler should be in balance.

6. Move one loop to the 3-inch notch; move the other to the 8-inch notch. The ruler will be unbalanced. Add a third paper clip to the loop at 8 inches to balance the ruler.

7. Add a clip to the right loop to make a total of 4 clips and move it to the 7-inch notch. Balance the ruler by moving the left loop to the 4-inch notch.

8. Move the right loop to the 10-inch notch and add two clips for a total of six. How many clips must hang from the loop at the 4-inch notch to make the ruler balance?

Observations

The ruler will balance if the units of weight times the units of length are equal for each side of the ruler. When six clips are hung 4 inches from the center (at the 10-inch notch) the units of weight times units of length equal 6×4 or 24. Thus the number of clips hung 2 inches from center (at the 4-inch notch) must be 12.

EXPERIMENT 3

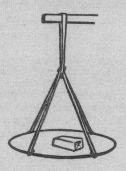

Apparatus

piece of wood, 30 inches high, thick enough to stand by itself
strip of wood, 6 inches long, ½ inch wide
hammer and nails
scissors
piece of heavy cardboard, 8 inches square
piece of string, 48 inches long
rubber band (the "spring" of your scale)
4 4-ounce weights (A pound of butter divided into four sections makes good weights. Assure your mother that the butter will be returned to her in usable condition.)

Steps

1. Make a weighing pan by cutting a circle 6 inches in diameter from the cardboard. Punch four equidistant holes round the circle, near its circumference.

2. Cut the string in four equal pieces. Tie one end of each string to the holes. Tie the other ends together, hooking them over one end of the rubber band.

3. Make a holder for your weighing pan by hammering the smaller strip of wood to the larger one. The smaller strip should be placed at right angles to the larger, at or near the top, and should extend horizontally to the right or left at least 4½ inches.

4. Hang your weighing pan by its rubber band to the holder. The pan should hang free.

5. Place a 4-ounce weight on the pan. The rubber band will extend, thus lowering the pan. Mark the vertical piece of wood at the 4-ounce point.

6. Add the second 4-ounce weight and mark the wood at 8 ounces. Add the third weight and mark at 12 ounces; add the fourth and mark at 1 pound.

7. Cut one of the quarter-pound sections of butter in half. Place a 2-ounce weight in the weighing pan and mark the wood at 2 ounces. Combine this weight with 4 ounces, 8 ounces, and 12 ounces and mark their locations (6, 10, and 14 ounces) on the wood. The spring scale can now be used to determine the weight of objects between 2 ounces and 1 pound.

Observations

When an object is weighed with a spring balance, the earth's gravitational attraction for the object stretches the spring. At the point where the opposing force set up by the stretched spring equals the earth's pull on the object, the stretching stops. But gravitational pull varies—it is less strong on a mountain top than at sea level. Thus the spring scale would register one weight for an object on Mount Washington and another weight for that same object in Atlantic City. (Beam balances are not subject to this inaccuracy. Can you figure out why?)

APPENDIX

General Science

ADLER, IRVING. *Fire in Your Life*. The John Day Co., 1955.

BARR, GEORGE. *Research Ideas for Young Scientists*. Whittlesey House, 1958.

BARR, GEORGE. *More Research Ideas for Young Scientists*. Whittlesey House, 1961.

BEAUCHAMP, WILBUR L., JOHN C. MAYFIELD, and JOE YOUNG WEST. *Science Problems 3*. Scott, Foresman & Co., 1957.

CALDER, RITCHIE. *Science in Our Lives*. Signet, 1955.

CARROLL, FRANKLIN B., SAM ADAMS, and LEE MONCRIEF HARRISON. *Science in the Universe*. The John C. Winston Co., 1958.

COOPER, ELIZABETH K. *Science in Your Own Back Yard*. Harcourt, Brace & Co., 1958.

DAVIS, HELEN MILES. *Science Exhibits*. Science Service, Inc., 1959.

DAVIS, HELEN MILES. *Scientific Instruments You Can Make*. Science Service, Inc., 1959.

DAVIS, IRA C., JOHN BURNETT, and E. WAYNE GROSS. *Science 2*. Holt, Rinehart and Winston, Inc., 1962.

GAMOW, GEORGE. *One, Two, Three . . . Infinity*. The Viking Press, 1954.

GOLDSTEIN, PHILIP. *How to Do an Experiment*. Harcourt, Brace & Co., 1957.

HERBERT, DON. *Mr. Wizard's Experiments for Young Scientists*. Doubleday & Co., 1959.

KADESCH, DR. ROBERT R. *The Crazy Cantilever and Other Science Experiments*. Harper & Bros., 1961.

LEWELLEN, JOHN. *The Boy Scientist*. Golden Press, Inc., 1955.

MILGROM, HARRY. *Explorations in Science*. E. P. Dutton & Co., 1961.

MOORE, SHIRLEY (ed.). *Science Projects Handbook*. Ballantine Books, 1960.

MOORE, SHIRLEY, and JUDITH VIORST. *Wonderful World of Science*. Bantam Books, 1961.

SWEEZEY, KENNETH M. *After-Dinner Science*. McGraw-Hill Book Co., 1961.

UNESCO. *Unesco Source Book for Science Teaching*. UNESCO, 1956.

VISNER, HAROLD, and ADELAIDE HECHTLINGER. *Simple Science Experiments*. Franklin Pub. Co., 1960.

WATSON, JANE WERNER. *The World of Science*. Golden Press, Inc., 1958.

WYLER, ROSE. *The First Book of Science Experiments*. Franklin Watts, Inc., 1952.

Biology

AMES, GERALD, and ROSE WYLER. *The Giant Golden Book of Biology*. Golden Press, Inc., 1961.

ATKIN, J. MYRON, and R. WILL BURNETT. *Working with Animals*. Rinehart & Co., 1959.

ATKIN, J. MYRON, and R. WILL BURNETT. *Working with Plants*. Rinehart & Co., 1959.

BARKER, WILL. *Familiar Insects of America*. Harper & Bros., 1960.

BEELER, NELSON F., and FRANKLYN M. BRANLEY. *Experiments with a Microscope*. Crowell, 1957.

BROWN, VINSON. *How to Make a Home Nature Museum*. Little, Brown & Co., 1954.

CHAMBERS, ROBERT WARNER, and ALMA SMITH PAYNE. *From Cell to Test Tube*. Charles Scribner's Sons, 1960.

COSGROVE, MARGARET. *Strange Worlds under a Microscope*. Dodd, Mead & Co., 1962.

DOERING, HARALD. *A Bee Is Born*. Sterling Pub. Co., 1962.

FITZPATRICK, FREDERICK L., and THOMAS D. BAIN. *Living Things*. Henry Holt & Co., 1958.

GLEMSER, BERNARD. *All About the Human Body*. Random House, 1958.

GORAN, MORRIS. *Experimental Biology for Boys*. John F. Rider Pub., Inc., 1961.

HANAUER, ETHEL. *Biology for Children*. Sterling Pub. Co., 1962.

HEISS, ELWOOD D., and RICHARD H. LAPE. *Biology, a Basic Science*. D. Van Nostrand Co., 1961.

MCBAIN, W. N., and R. C. JOHNSON. *The Science of Ourselves*. Harper & Row, 1962.

RAVIELLI, ANTHONY. *Wonders of the Human Body*. The Viking Press, 1954.

RIEDMAN, SARAH R. *The World Through Your Senses*. Abelard-Schuman, 1962.

WITHERSPOON, JAMES DONALD, and REBECCA HUTTO WITHERSPOON. *The Living Laboratory*. Doubleday & Co., 1960.

ZIM, HERBERT S. *Plants*. Harcourt, Brace & Co., 1947.

ZIM, HERBERT S. *Our Senses and How They Work*. William Morrow & Co., 1956.

Chemistry

ASIMOV, ISAAC. *Building Blocks of the Universe*. Abelard-Schuman, 1961.

BATTISTA, O. A. *The Challenge of Chemistry*. The John C. Winston Co., 1959.

COOPER, ELIZABETH K. *Discovering Chemistry*. Harcourt, Brace & Co., 1959.

DAVIS, HELEN MILES. *The Chemical Elements*. Ballantine Books, 1959.

DULL, CHARLES E., H. CLARK METCALFE, and JOHN E. WILLIAMS. *Modern Chemistry* (2nd ed.). Holt, Rinehart & Winston, 1962.

FEIFER, NATHAN. *Let's Explore Chemistry*. Sentinel, 1959.

FLIEDNER, LEONARD J., and LOUIS TEICHMAN. *Chemistry, Man's Servant*. Allyn and Bacon, Inc., 1958.

FREEMAN, IRA M. *All About the Wonders of Chemistry*. Random House, 1954.

FREEMAN, MAE, and IRA FREEMAN. *Fun with Chemistry*. Random House, Inc., 1962.

GORAN, MORRIS. *Experimental Chemistry for Boys*. John F. Rider, Pub., 1961.

HAWK, BURTON L. *Organic Chemistry for the Home Lab*. Science Service, Inc., 1956.

HAWK, BURTON L. *Experimenting with Chemistry*. Science Service, Inc., 1957.

HESS, FRED C. *Chemistry Made Simple*. Made Simple, 1955.

HOLMES, HARRY N. *Out of the Test Tube*. Emerson, 1957.

HUTTON, KENNETH. *Chemistry: The Conquest of Materials*. Pelican, 1961.

IRWIN, KEITH G. *The Romance of Chemistry from Ancient Alchemy to Nuclear Fission*. The Viking Press, 1959.

MEYER, JEROME S. *Picture Book of Chemistry*. Lothrop, Lee & Shepard Co., 1957.

NEWCOMB, ELLSWORTH, and HUGH KENNY. *Alchemy to Atoms*. G. P. Putnam's Sons, 1961.

SEABORG, GLENN T., and EVANS G. VALENS. *Elements of the Universe*. E. P. Dutton & Co., 1958.

WEAVER, ELBERT C., and LAURENCE S. FOSTER. *Chemistry for Our Times*. McGraw-Hill Book Co., 1960.

Numbers

ADLER, IRVING. *Magic House of Numbers*. John Day Co., 1957.

COURANT, RICHARD, and HERBERT ROBBINS. *What Is Mathematics?* Oxford Univ. Press, 1941.

CROWDER, NORMAN A. *The Arithmetic of Computers*. Doubleday & Co., 1960.

HOGBEN, LANCELOT. *Mathematics for the Million* (3rd ed.). W. W. Norton & Co., 1951.

HOGBEN, LANCELOT. *The Wonderful World of Mathematics*. Doubleday & Co., 1955.

JOHNSON, DONOVAN A., and WILLIAM H. GLENN. *Exploring Mathematics on Your Own*. Doubleday & Co., 1961.

LIEBER, LILLIAN R. *The Education of T. C. Mits*. W. W. Norton & Co., 1944.

LIEBER, LILLIAN R. *Take a Number*. Ronald Press Co., 1946.

MERRILL, HELEN A. *Mathematical Excursions*. Dover, 1957.

MEYER, JEROME S. *Fun with Mathematics*. World Pub. Co., 1952.

MOTT-SMITH, GEOFFREY. *How to Use the Arithmetic You Know.* Sterling Pub. Co., 1960.

RADEMACHER, HANS, and OTTO TOEPLITZ. *The Enjoyment of Mathematics.* Princeton Univ. Press, 1957.

RAVIELLI, ANTHONY. *An Adventure in Geometry.* The Viking Press, 1957.

RECKLESS, MAYTSCHERL W. *Understanding Arithmetic.* Prentice-Hall, Inc., 1961.

REID, CONSTANCE. *From Zero to Infinity.* Apollo, 1961.

RUCHLIS, HY, and JACK ENGLEHART. *The Story of Mathematics.* Harvey House Pub., 1958.

STICKER, HENRY. *How to Calculate Quickly.* Dover, 1955.

VERGARA, WILLIAM C. *Mathematics in Everyday Things.* Signet, 1962.

Physics

ADLER, IRVING. *The Secret of Light.* International Pub. Co., 1952.

ATKIN, J. MYRON, and R. WILL BURNETT. *Electricity and Magnetism.* Holt, 1958.

BEELER, NELSON F. *Experiments in Sound.* Thomas Y. Crowell Co., 1961.

BEISER, GERMAINE, and ARTHUR BEISER. *Physics for Everybody.* Everyman, 1960.

BENDER, ALFRED. *Let's Explore with the Electron.* Sentinel, 1960.

BOYLAN, PAUL J. *Elements of Physics.* Allyn & Bacon, 1958.

DOAN, WILLARD. *Experimental Electricity for Boys.* John F. Rider Pub., 1959.

FARADAY, MICHAEL. *On the Various Forces of Nature.* The Viking Press, 1960.

FREEMAN, IRA M. *Physics Made Simple.* Made Simple, 1954.

FREEMAN, IRA M. *All About Electricity.* Random House, 1957.

FREEMAN, IRA M. *All About Sound and Ultrasonics.* Random House, 1961.

HABER, HEINZ. *Our Friend the Atom.* Golden Press, Inc., 1956.

IRVING, ROBERT. *Energy and Power.* Alfred A. Knopf, 1958.

IRVING, ROBERT. *Sound and Ultrasonics.* Alfred A. Knopf, 1959.

KNIGHT, DAVID C. *The First Book of Sound.* Franklin Watts, Inc., 1960.

MEYER, JEROME S. *Prisms and Lenses.* World Pub. Co., 1959.

MORGAN, ALFRED. *The Boy's Third Book of Radio and Electronics.* Charles Scribner's Sons, 1962.

NATIONAL SCIENCE TEACHERS ASSOCIATION. *Experiments with Radioactivity.* National Science Teachers Association, 1958.

NELSON, OLE A., and JOHN G. WINANS. *Everyday Physics.* Ginn and Co., 1952.

PASCHEL, HERBERT P. *The First Book of Color.* Franklin Watts, Inc., 1959.

RUCHLIS, HY. *Orbit.* Harper & Bros., 1958.

RUCHLIS, HY. *The Wonders of Heat Energy*. Harper & Bros., 1961.

VIORST, JUDITH. *Projects: Space*. Washington Square Press, Inc., 1962.

Weather

ANTOINE, TEX. *Wonders of the Weather*. Dodd, Mead & Co., 1962.

BATTAN, LOUIS J. *Cloud Physics and Cloud Seeding*. Doubleday & Co., 1962.

BELL, THELMA HARRINGTON. *Thunderstorm*. The Viking Press, 1960.

BOLTON, JOE. *The Wind and the Weather*. Thomas Y. Crowell Co., 1957.

LAIRD, CHARLES, and RUTH LAIRD. *Weathercasting*. Prentice-Hall, Inc., 1955.

MILGROM, HARRY. *The Adventure Book of Weather*. Capitol Pub. Co., 1959.

PILKINGTON, ROGER. *The Ways of the Air*. Criterion Books, 1962.

SCHNEIDER, HERMAN. *Everyday Weather and How It Works*. Whittlesey House, 1951.

TANNEHILL, IVAN RAY. *All About the Weather*. Random House, 1953.

WOLFE, LOUIS. *Probing the Atmosphere*. G. P. Putnam's Sons, 1961.

WYLER, ROSE. *The First Book of Weather*. Franklin Watts, Inc., 1956.

1. A single ATOM is the tiniest particle of any chemical element that can exist by itself and retain the qualities that mark it as that element.

2. All material things in the universe known to our senses are composed of atoms of CHEMICAL ELEMENTS.

3. Substances composed of more than one element are known as COMPOUNDS. Atoms attract and hold each other by electrical forces.

4. The smallest theoretical unit of a compound, composed of two or more atoms, is known as a MOLECULE; some elements are also normally found as molecules or crystals.

5. The smallest actual units of crystalline compounds found by use of microscopes and electron microscopes seem to be structures built up of the different atoms alternating in three-dimensional patterns to form the CRYSTAL LATTICE.

6. There were believed to be 92 CHEMICAL ELEMENTS, from hydrogen, $_1H^1$, the lightest, to uranium, $_{92}U^{238}$, the heaviest, before the discovery of nuclear fission.

7. Two new elements, NEPTUNIUM, $_{93}Np^{239}$, formed by the neutron bombardment of uranium 238, and PLUTONIUM, $_{94}Pu^{238}$, formed by deuteron bombardment of uranium 238, were discovered two years thereafter.

8. Additional new elements have since been created by atomic bombardment, using the cores of light elements as projectiles. As of 1961, elements through 103 have been added, the ones beyond plutonium being: AMERICIUM, CURIUM, BERKELIUM, CALIFORNIUM, EINSTEINIUM, FERMIUM, MENDELEVIUM, NOBELIUM (name in dispute), and LAWRENCIUM.

9. When elements are represented, as above, by their chemical symbols, the subscript number is the ATOMIC NUMBER. This is different for each element. The superscript number is the MASS NUMBER, and also the total number of protons plus neutrons, or the ATOMIC WEIGHT rounded off to the nearest whole number.

10. All atoms are composed of standard interchangeable parts. These are PROTONS, NEUTRONS and ELECTRONS.

11. Protons and neutrons make up the NUCLEUS of the atom. Collectively, they are called nucleons. The structure of the atom is comparable to that of the solar system. The nucleus corresponds to the sun at the center. The planets are electrons.

12. The ELECTRONS, light in weight and some distance away from the nucleus of the atom, revolve around the nucleus. They are held in their courses by electric attraction.

13. The proton has a POSITIVE charge of electricity, the electron has a NEGATIVE charge equal and opposite to the positive charge of the proton. The neutron has no charge at all.

14. The proton and the neutron each have a mass of about one ATOMIC MASS UNIT. Each is about 1800 times heavier than the electron.

15. ATOMIC NUMBER is the measure of the electric charge on, or number of protons in, the nucleus of the atom.

16. The difference in CHEMICAL PROPERTIES of the elements is caused by difference in the number of electrons, which in turn is caused by difference in the number of protons in the nucleus. The number of electrons and protons are equal in an electrically neutral atom.

17. Chemical VALENCE, or combining power, is governed primarily by the electrons in the outermost orbits of each atom. Characteristics of transition elements are also governed by electrons in the next-to-outermost shell.

18. MASS NUMBER is the total number of protons and neutrons in the nucleus.

19. ATOMIC WEIGHT is the measure of the atom's mass.

20. Different atoms of the SAME ELEMENT are sometimes found to have DIFFERENT ATOMIC WEIGHTS. Such atoms are called ISOTOPES.

21. In all other ways ISOTOPES are chemical twins, alike except for weight. They have the same ATOMIC NUMBER, but have different numbers of neutrons.

22. Every element has been found to have a number of isotopes, some STABLE, some RADIOACTIVE.

23. Atomic weights of individual ISOTOPES are usually given relative to the most abundant isotope of oxygen, $_8O^{16}$, taken as 16.00000 atomic mass units (physicists' scale).

24. There are two scales of ATOMIC WEIGHTS, physical and chemical. In the physical atomic weight scale, the mass of an atom of O^{16} is used as the standard and assigned a mass of 16.00000 units. In the chemical atomic weight scale, the atomic weight of the natural isotopic mixture of oxygen, which contains O^{16} and O^{18} in addition to O^{16}, is assigned the value of 16.00000.

25. Different elements, quite distinct in chemical behavior, may have isotopes of the same atomic weight. There are $_{92}U^{238}$, $_{93}Np^{238}$, $_{94}Pu^{238}$, $_{95}Am^{238}$ and $_{96}Cm^{238}$, all with different properties. Such atoms are called ISOBARS.

26. It is the NEUTRON which figures in the transmutations that give atomic power from uranium. Neutrons can PENETRATE to the nucleus of heavy atoms when charged particles would be repelled by charges in the atom. The neutron is absorbed by the nucleus to form a heavier nucleus that is frequently unstable. If it is unstable, it then decomposes radioactively, usually emitting an electron and changing to a different element one atomic number greater.

27. The HYDROGEN atom, $_1H^1$, has just one proton as its nucleus, with one electron circling around it. Hydrogen's atomic weight and atomic number are each one.

28. Hydrogen has a rare istotope, $_1H^2$, that is just like ordinary hydrogen except it is twice as heavy. It is known as "heavy hydrogen" and sometimes as DEUTERIUM (Symbol: D). Its compound with oxygen is called "heavy water."

29. The nucleus of DEUTERIUM, called a DEUTERON, contains one proton and one neutron. The atomic number of heavy hydrogen is one, corresponding to one proton. The atomic weight is two, corresponding to the two heavy particles, proton and neutron. A third form of hydrogen, the RADIOACTIVE isotope TRITIUM, $_1H^3$, is composed of one proton and two neutrons.

30. HELIUM, $_2He^4$, has two protons and two neutrons in its nucleus. The two protons correspond to helium's atomic number two. The combined weights of protons and neutrons in the nucleus give helium its atomic weight four. Two electrons, held in their orbits by the two protons, revolve around the nucleus.

31. Helium 4 at temperatures near absolute zero is a liquid with most remarkable properties and is the only known SUPERFLUID.

32. Helium also has a rare LIGHTER ISOTOPE, $_2He^3$, composed of two protons and one neutron.

33. Uranium has a number of isotopes. The most abundant, whose atomic weight is 238, was used to produce the new elements. U-235 was used to make the first ATOMIC BOMB.

34. The isotope U-235 and the element plutonium can be used for bombs because they are capable of FISSION after absorbing a neutron.

35. When fission occurs, the nucleus of the atom SPLITS into two (occasionally more) lighter elements, with release of nuclear energy.

36. In some recent experiments with high-powered cyclotrons, even more thorough fragmentation of atomic nuclei resulted. This process, resulting in many light elements, was named SPALLATION. General laws are now known that explain the processes by which atoms and nuclear particles unite and divide to form isotopes of particular mass, form and radioactive lifetimes.

37. FUSION, the process by which stars obtain their energy, is a nuclear reaction in which light nuclei combine to form a nucleus of a higher mass number, releasing large amounts of energy. The process can be said to be the opposite of nuclear fission. Fusion forms the basis of the hydrogen bomb. The possibility that the virtually limitless fuel locked as forms of hydrogen in the world's ocean can be tapped by the controlled release of fusion is under extensive investigation throughout the world.

38. MESONS are short-lived particles intermediate in mass between electrons and nucleons. HYPERONS are particles intermediate in mass between nucleons and deuterons. Their role in holding particles together in the atomic nucleus is being investigated.

39. The VOLUME of an atom is determined by the orbits of its outermost revolving electrons. Only a small fraction of the size of an atom is actually occupied by the protons, neutrons and electrons,

somewhat as the space occupied by the sun, the earth and other planets is only a small part of our solar system.

40. In spite of all the unoccupied space, an atom is quite IM-PENETRABLE to other atoms and to larger bodies. The electrons revolve millions of times a second, and keep everything out of the space within quite as effectively as though they were everywhere at once.

41. The things that can get inside an atom easily are protons, neutrons or electrons and fragments of other atoms. They must be shot with sufficient SPEED.

42. RADIATION is wave motion, known to us as the electromagnetic waves used for radio transmission, heat, light, X-rays, gamma rays, and as beams of atomic particles. Extremely tiny particles act like waves.

43. Three types of rays are given off by radioactive substances. ALPHA particles are high-speed nuclei of helium atoms. BETA particles are high-speed electrons. GAMMA RAYS are electromagnetic radiations similar to X-rays and light.

44. Of these, only the gamma rays used to be called radiation, and even these act very much like particles because of their short wavelength. Such a "particle" or quantum of electromagnetic radiation is called a PHOTON.

45. All atoms, when excited by high temperatures or by electric discharge, may emit light rays. These light rays, sorted according to wavelength with spectrographs, make up the SPECTRA characteristic of the elements. Most of our information about the outer structure of atoms is derived from these spectra.

46. Electrically charged particles, such as electrons, may be bent out of their straight-line paths by the influence of a magnet. This principle is used in the construction of the CYCLOTRON.

47. POSITRONS are like electrons, but are bent in the opposite direction because their charges are positive instead of negative. Thus a positron is an "anti-electron."

48. Scientists now know that atomic particles as well as mesons and hyperons have so-called "anti" forms, which denote another particle with most of the same characteristics but differing in others, including charge and magnetic moment. When normal matter collides with ANTI-MATTER, both are annihilated and tremendous amounts of energy are released.

49. The kind of rays emitted and the HALF LIFE (the time in which half the radioactivity decays) are constant characteristics of each radioactive isotope, and are used to identify that isotope.

50. In general, the gamma rays are very PENETRATING, beta rays less so, and alpha particles are easily stopped. Even though the alpha and beta rays are not very penetrating, they have enormous speed.

51. ENERGY is capacity to do work. It is work stored up for future use.

52. If you raise a weight to a height above the ground and suspend it there by some device, the work you put into raising it can be stored there indefinitely as POTENTIAL ENERGY. It will be there, ready, whenever you decide to release it.

53. The energy that a moving body has because it is in motion is called KINETIC ENERGY. The kinetic energy of any particle depends upon its mass and its velocity. When the moving particle strikes an object, work is done.

54. Particles of atomic size have kinetic energy arising from several different kinds of MOTION. All atoms are constantly in motion.

55. If the atoms are so dispersed that the material constituting them is a GAS, that gas will exert pressure on all sides of the container holding it, because of the motion of the gas molecules.

56. Atoms composing an element that will combine readily with another element, as hydrogen or carbon will combine with oxygen, have incomplete arrangements of the outer electrons in their systems. These incomplete arrangements allow CHEMICAL COMBINATION to take place when elements with suitable combining powers are brought together.

57. When chemical reactions occur, energy can be absorbed or released in the process. Reactions in which energy is absorbed are called ENDOTHERMIC REACTIONS; those in which energy is released are called EXOTHERMIC REACTIONS.

58. Chemical energy, electricity and heat are all forms of ENERGY. Potential and kinetic energy may be distinguished in each case.

59. These energies all arise from motion of the atom as a whole, or motion resulting from attractions and repulsions between the outer ELECTRONS of the atom's structure.

60. Energy resulting from changes in the nucleus of the atom was unknown until the discovery of RADIOACTIVITY.

61. Radioactive isotopes undergo SPONTANEOUS breaking up of their nuclei, giving off beta, alpha or gamma radiation. Loss of these particles causes the radioactive isotopes to change into isotopes of other elements.

62. The energies shown in these TRANSMUTATIONS are millions of times greater than the kinetic energies the molecules of a gas have by reason of their motion when heated. They are about a million times greater than the energy changes per atom in chemical reactions.

63. The property of matter that connects it with motion is INERTIA. Inertia is resistance to change of motion and is the measure of the MASS of an object.

64. One conclusion that appeared early in the development of the theory of RELATIVITY is that the mass of a moving body increases as its speed is increased.

65. This increase implies an equivalence between an increase in energy of motion of a body (kinetic energy) and an increase in its MASS.

66. It is for this reason that Einstein suggested that studies of radioactivity might show the EQUIVALENCE of mass and energy.

67. Einstein's statement is that the amount of energy, E, equivalent to a mass, m, is given by the equation $E = mc^2$, where c is the VELOCITY OF LIGHT.

68. From this equation, one kilogram (2.2 pounds) of matter, if CONVERTED entirely into energy, would give 25 billion kilowatt hours of energy.

69. The heat produced by BURNING one kilogram of coal is 8.5 kilowatt hours of energy.

70. Two axioms of physics state: (1) MATTER can be neither created nor destroyed; (2) ENERGY can be neither created nor destroyed. For all practical purposes they were true and separate principles until about 1940.

71. It is now known that they are, in fact, TWO PHASES of a single principle, for we have discovered that energy may sometimes be converted into matter and matter into energy.

72. Such conversion is observed in the phenomenon of nuclear FISSION, a process in which atomic nuclei split into fragments with the release of an enormous amount of energy.

73. The extreme size of the CONVERSION FACTOR explains why the equivalence of mass and energy is never observed in ordinary chemical combustion.

74. We now believe the heat given off in chemical COMBUSTION has mass associated with it, but this mass is so small it cannot be detected by the most sensitive balances available.

75. From the standpoint of the Laws of the Conservation of Matter and of Energy alone, transformation of matter into energy results in the DESTRUCTION of matter and CREATION of energy.

(*Compiled originally by Helen M. Davis; revised 1961.*)

TABLES AND CHARTS

■ HOUSEHOLD CHEMICALS

Household Name	Chemical Name	Formula
ammonia water	ammonium hydroxide	NH_4OH
aspirin	acetylsalicylic acid	$C_6H_4(OCOCH_3)COOH$
baking soda	sodium bicarbonate	$NaHCO_3$
cane sugar	sucrose	$C_{12}H_{22}O_{11}$
chalk	calcium carbonate	$CaCO_3$
charcoal	wood carbon	C
dry ice	solid carbon dioxide	CO_2
Epsom salts	magnesium sulfate	$MgSO_4 \bullet 7H_2O$
lye	sodium hydroxide	$NaOH$
marble	calcium carbonate	$CaCO_3$
milk of magnesia	magnesium hydroxide	$Mg(OH)_2$
moth balls	naphthalene	$C_{10}H_8$
peroxide	hydrogen peroxide	H_2O_2
rouge	ferric oxide	Fe_2O_3
salt	sodium chloride	$NaCl$
sand	silicon dioxide	SiO_2
vinegar	dilute acetic acid	$HC_2H_3O_2$

■ THE PLANT KINGDOM

Subkingdom Thallophyta

Phylum	Class	Order	Description
Cyanophyta			algae
Euglenophyta			algae
Chlorophyta			algae
Chrysophyta			algae
Pyrrophyta			algae
Phaeophyta			algae
Rhodophyta			algae
Schizophyta			fungi
Eumycophyta			fungi
Myxomycophyta			fungi

Subkingdom Embryophyta

Phylum	Class	Order	Description
Bryophyta			
	Musci		mosses
	Hepaticae		liverworts
	Anthocerotae		hornworts
Tracheophyta			vascular plants

Subphylum	Class	Order	Description
Psilopsida			
	Psilophytineae		
		Psilophytales	fossils
		Psilotales	psilophytes
Lycopsida			club mosses
	Lycopodineae		
		Lycopodiales	club mosses
		Selaginellales	club mosses
		Lepidodendrales	fossils
		Pleuromeiales	fossils
		Isoetales	quillworts
Sphenopsida			horsetails
	Equisetineae		
		Hyeniales	fossils
		Sphenophyllales	fossils
		Equisetales	horsetails
Pteropsida			
	Filicineae		ferns
		Coenopteridales	fossils
		Ophioglossales	adder's tongue fern
		Marattiales	marattiaceous ferns
		Filicales	true ferns
	Gymnospermae		conifers and related plants
	Subclass Cycadophytae		
		Cycadofilicales	fossils
		Bennettitales	fossils
		Cycadales	cycads
	Coniferophytae		
		Cordaitales	fossils
		Ginkgoales	ginko tree
		Coniferales	conifers
		Gnetales	**Ephedra, Gnetum, Welwitschia**
	Angiospermae		flowering plants
	Subclass Dicotyledoneae		dicots
	Monocotyledoneae		monocots

■ THE ANIMAL KINGDOM

Subkingdom Protozoa—Single-celled Animals

Phylum	Class	Description
Protozoa		
	Flagellata	flagellates
	Sarcodina	rhizopods
	Sporozoa	sporozoans
	Ciliata	ciliates
	Suctoria	suctorians

Subkingdom Metazoa—Multi-celled Animals

Phylum	Class	Description
Mesozoa		mesozoans
Porifera		sponges
	Calcarea	calcareous sponges
	Hyalospongiae	glass sponges
	Demospongiae	horny or keratinous sponges
Coelenterata		coelenterates
	Hydrozoa	hydrozoans
	Scyphozoa	oceanic jellyfish
	Anthozoa	corals, sea anemones, sea fans, sea pens
Ctenophora		comb jellies
Platyhelminthes		flatworms
	Turbellaria	flatworms
	Trematoda	parasitic flukes
	Cestoda	parasitic tapeworms
Nemertina		nemertean worms
Nemathelminthes		roundworms
Rotifera		rotifers or wheel animalcules
Gastrotricha		gastrotrichs
Kinorhyncha		kinorhynchids
Nematomorpha		hair worms
Acanthocephala		thorny-headed worms
Entoprocta		moss animals
Priapulida		priapulids
Annelida		
	Polychaeta	polychaetes
	Oligochaeta	oligochaetes
	Hirudinea	leeches
Echluroidea		echiurids
Sipunculoidea		peanut worms
Mollusca		mollusks
	Amphineura	chitons
	Scaphopoda	tooth shells
	Gastropoda	snails, slugs, limpets
	Pelecypoda	clams, oysters, mussels, shipworms
	Cephalopoda	squids, octopuses, nautiluses
Bryozoa		moss animals
Brachiopoda		lamp shells
Phoronida		phoronids
Arthropoda		arthropods
	Onychophora	onychophorans
	Crustacea	crustaceans
	Trilobita	fossils
	Meristomata	horseshoe crabs
	Arachnida	arachnids
	Diplopoda	millipedes
	Chilopoda	centipedes
	Insecta	insects

Phylum	Class	Description
Echinodermata		ectoderms
	Asteroidea	starfish
	Ophiuroidea	brittle stars
	Echinoidea	sea and heart urchins
	Holothuroidea	sea cucumber
	Crinoidea	sea lilies
Chaetognatha		arrow worms
Pogonophora		beard worms
Chordata		
Subphylum		
Hemichordata		tongue worms, acorn worms
Urochordata		tunicates
Cephalochordata		lancelets
Vertebrata		vertebrates
Superclass		
Pisces		
	Agnatha	lamprey eels, hag fishes
	Chondrichthyes	sharks, rays
	Osteichthyes	bony fish
Superclass		
Tetrapoda		
	Amphibia	frogs, salamanders, toads
	Reptilia	turtles, snakes, lizards, etc.
	Aves	birds
	Mammalia	mammals

■ RELATIVE HUMIDITY TABLE

Dry-bulb temperature

DIFFERENCE BETWEEN WET- AND DRY-BULB TEMPERATURES

	1	2	3	4	5	6	7	8	9	10	11	12	13	14
98	96	93	89	86	82	79	76	72	69	66	63	60	57	54
96	96	93	89	85	82	78	75	72	68	65	62	59	57	54
94	96	93	89	85	81	78	75	71	68	65	62	59	56	53
92	96	92	88	85	81	78	74	71	67	64	61	58	55	52
90	96	92	88	84	81	77	74	70	67	63	60	57	54	51
88	96	92	88	84	80	77	73	69	66	63	59	56	53	50
86	96	92	88	84	80	76	72	69	65	62	58	55	52	49
84	96	92	87	83	79	76	72	68	64	61	57	54	51	47
82	96	91	87	83	79	75	71	67	64	60	56	53	49	46
80	96	91	87	83	79	74	70	66	63	59	55	52	48	45
78	95	91	86	82	78	74	70	66	62	58	54	50	47	43
76	95	91	86	82	78	73	69	65	61	57	53	49	45	42
74	95	90	86	81	77	72	68	64	60	56	52	48	44	40
72	95	90	85	80	76	71	67	63	58	54	50	46	42	38
70	95	90	85	80	75	71	66	62	57	53	49	44	40	36
68	95	90	84	79	75	70	65	60	56	51	47	43	38	34
66	95	89	84	79	74	69	64	59	54	50	45	41	36	32
64	94	89	83	78	73	68	63	58	53	48	43	39	34	30
62	94	88	83	77	72	67	61	56	51	46	41	37	32	27
60	94	88	82	77	71	65	60	55	50	44	39	34	29	25
58	94	88	82	76	70	64	59	53	48	42	37	31	26	22
56	94	87	81	75	69	63	57	51	46	40	35	29	24	19
54	93	87	80	74	68	61	55	49	43	38	32	26	21	15
52	93	86	79	73	66	60	54	47	41	35	29	23	17	12
50	93	86	79	72	65	59	52	45	38	32	26	20	14	8
48	92	85	77	70	63	56	49	42	36	29	22	16	10	4
46	92	84	77	69	62	54	47	40	33	26	19	12	6	—
44	92	84	75	68	60	52	45	37	29	22	15	8	—	—
42	91	83	74	66	58	50	42	34	26	18	—	—	—	—
40	91	82	73	65	56	47	39	30	—	—	—	—	—	—

This table is in degrees Fahrenheit.

■ CENTIGRADE TO FAHRENHEIT CONVERSION TABLE

°C	°F	°C	°F	°C	°F	°C	°F
0	32						
1	34	26	79	51	124	76	169
2	36	27	81	52	126	77	171
3	37	28	82	53	127	78	172
4	39	29	84	54	129	79	174
5	41	30	86	55	131	80	176
6	43	31	88	56	133	81	178
7	45	32	90	57	135	82	180
8	46	33	91	58	136	83	181
9	48	34	93	59	138	84	183
10	50	35	95	60	140	85	185
11	52	36	97	61	142	86	187
12	54	37	99	62	144	87	189
13	55	38	100	63	145	88	190
14	57	39	102	64	147	89	192
15	59	40	104	65	149	90	194
16	61	41	106	66	151	91	196
17	63	42	108	67	153	92	198
18	64	43	109	68	154	93	199
19	66	44	111	69	156	94	201
20	68	45	113	70	158	95	203
21	70	46	115	71	160	96	205
22	72	47	117	72	162	97	207
23	73	48	118	73	163	98	208
24	75	49	120	74	165	99	210
25	77	50	122	75	167	100	212

■ WEIGHTS AND MEASURES

LINEAR MEASURE

12 inches	1 foot
3 feet	1 yard
5280 feet	1 mile

SQUARE MEASURE

144 square inches	1 square foot
9 square feet	1 square yard
640 acres	1 square mile

LIQUID MEASURE

4 gills	1 pint
2 pints	1 quart
4 quarts	1 gallon

DRY MEASURE

2 pints	1 quart
8 quarts	1 peck
32 quarts	1 bushel

The Metric System

LENGTH

10 millimeters	1 centimeter
10 centimeters	1 decimeter
10 decimeters	1 meter
10 meters	1 decameter
10 decameters	1 hectometer
10 hectometers	1 kilometer
10 kilometers	1 myriameter

WEIGHT

10 milligrams	1 centigram
10 centigrams	1 decigram
10 decigrams	1 gram
10 grams	1 decagram
10 decagrams	1 hectogram
10 hectograms	1 kilogram
1000 kilograms	1 metric ton

Conversions

1 inch	2.54 centimeters
1 foot	30.48 centimeters
1 quart liquid	0.9463 liter

1 centimeter	0.3937 inch
1 meter	39.37 inches
1 liter	1.057 quarts liquid

■ TABLE OF SQUARES AND SQUARE ROOTS

N	N²	√N	N	N²	√N	N	N²	√N
1	1	1.000	51	2 601	7.141	101	10 201	10.050
2	4	1.414	52	2 704	7.211	102	10 404	10.100
3	9	1.732	53	2 809	7.280	103	10 609	10.149
4	16	2.000	54	2 916	7.348	104	10 816	10.198
5	25	2.236	55	3 025	7.416	105	11 025	10.247
6	36	2.449	56	3 136	7.483	106	11 236	10.296
7	49	2.646	57	3 249	7.550	107	11 449	10.344
8	64	2.828	58	3 364	7.616	108	11 664	10.392
9	81	3.000	59	3 481	7.681	109	11 881	10.440
10	100	3.162	60	3 600	7.746	110	12 100	10.488
11	121	3.317	61	3 721	7.810	111	12 321	10.536
12	144	3.464	62	3 844	7.874	112	12 544	10.583
13	169	3.606	63	3 969	7.937	113	12 769	10.630
14	196	3.742	64	4 096	8.000	114	12 996	10.677
15	225	3.873	65	4 225	8.062	115	13 225	10.724
16	256	4.000	66	4 356	8.124	116	13 456	10.770
17	289	4.123	67	4 489	8.185	117	13 689	10.817
18	324	4.243	68	4 624	8.246	118	13 924	10.863
19	361	4.359	69	4 761	8.307	119	14 161	10.909
20	400	4.472	70	4 900	8.367	120	14 400	10.954
21	441	4.583	71	5 041	8.426	121	14 641	11.000
22	484	4.690	72	5 184	8.485	122	14 884	11.045
23	529	4.796	73	5 329	8.544	123	15 129	11.091
24	576	4.899	74	5 476	8.602	124	15 376	11.136
25	625	5.000	75	5 625	8.660	125	15 625	11.180
26	676	5.099	76	5 776	8.718	126	15 876	11.225
27	729	5.196	77	5 929	8.775	127	16 129	11.269
28	784	5.292	78	6 084	8.832	128	16 384	11.314
29	841	5.385	79	6 241	8.888	129	16 641	11.358
30	900	5.477	80	6 400	8.944	130	16 900	11.402
31	961	5.568	81	6 561	9.000	131	17 161	11.446
32	1 024	5.657	82	6 724	9.055	132	17 424	11.489
33	1 089	5.745	83	6 889	9.110	133	17 689	11.533
34	1 156	5.831	84	7 056	9.165	134	17 956	11.576
35	1 225	5.916	85	7 225	9.220	135	18 225	11.619
36	1 296	6.000	86	7 396	9.274	136	18 496	11.662
37	1 369	6.083	87	7 569	9.327	137	18 769	11.705
38	1 444	6.164	88	7 744	9.381	138	19 044	11.747
39	1 521	6.245	89	7 921	9.434	139	19 321	11.790
40	1 600	6.325	90	8 100	9.487	140	19 600	11.832
41	1 681	6.403	91	8 281	9.539	141	19 881	11.874
42	1 764	6.481	92	8 464	9.592	142	20 164	11.916
43	1 849	6.557	93	8 649	9.644	143	20 449	11.958
44	1 936	6.633	94	8 836	9.695	144	20 736	12.000
45	2 025	6.708	95	9 025	9.747	145	21 025	12.042
46	2 116	6.782	96	9 216	9.798	146	21 316	12.083
47	2 209	6.856	97	9 409	9.849	147	21 609	12.124
48	2 304	6.928	98	9 604	9.899	148	21 904	12.166
49	2 401	7.000	99	9 801	9.950	149	22 201	12.207
50	2 500	7.071	100	10 000	10.000	150	22 500	12.247

■ CHEMICAL ELEMENTS

Atomic weight is the average of an atom compared to an average atom of ordinary terrestrial oxygen as 16.

For the radioactive elements (with the exceptions of uranium, thorium, and radium), the mass number of either the isotope of longest half-life or the better known isotope (indicated with a star) is given.

Chemical element	Symbol	Atomic number	Atomic weight
Actinium	Ac	89	227
Aluminum	Al	13	26.98
Americium	Am	95	*243
Antimony	Sb	51	121.76
Argon	Ar	18	39.944
Arsenic	As	33	74.91
Astatine	At	85	210
Barium	Ba	56	137.36
Berkelium	Bk	97	*249
Beryllium	Be	4	9.013
Bismuth	Bi	83	209.00
Boron	B	5	10.82
Bromine	Br	35	79.916
Cadmium	Cd	48	112.41
Calcium	Ca	20	40.08
Californium	Cf	98	*249
Carbon	C	6	12.011
Cerium	Ce	58	140.13
Cesium	Cs	55	132.91
Chlorine	Cl	17	35.457
Chromium	Cr	24	52.01
Cobalt	Co	27	58.94
Copper	Cu	29	63.54
Curium	Cm	96	*247
Dysprosium	Dy	66	162.51
Einsteinium	E	99	*254
Element 102	......	102	*254
Erbium	Er	68	167.27
Europium	Eu	63	152.0
Fermium	Fm	100	*255
Fluorine	F	9	19.00
Francium	Fr	87	*223
Gadolinium	Gd	64	157.26
Gallium	Ga	31	69.72
Germanium	Ge	32	72.60
Gold	Au	79	197.0
Hafnium	Hf	72	178.50
Helium	He	2	4.003
Holmium	Ho	67	164.94
Hydrogen	H	1	1.0080
Indium	In	49	114.82
Iodine	I	53	126.91
Iridium	Ir	77	192.2
Iron	Fe	26	55.85
Krypton	Kr	36	83.80

179

Chemical element	Symbol	Atomic number	Atomic weight
Lanthanum	La	57	138.92
Lawrencium	Lw	103	*257
Lead	Pb	82	207.21
Lithium	Li	3	6.940
Lutetium	Lu	71	174.99
Magnesium	Mg	12	24.32
Manganese	Mn	25	54.94
Mendelevium	Mv	101	*256
Mercury	Hg	80	200.61
Molybdenum	Mo	42	95.95
Neodymium	Nd	60	144.27
Neon	Ne	10	20.183
Neptunium	Np	93	*237
Nickel	Ni	28	58.71
Niobium†	Nb	41	92.91
Nitrogen	N	7	14.008
Osmium	Os	76	190.2
Oxygen	O	8	16.0000
Palladium	Pd	46	106.4
Phosphorus	P	15	30.975
Platinum	Pt	78	195.09
Plutonium	Pu	94	*242
Polonium	Po	84	*210
Potassium	K	19	39.100
Praseodymium	Pr	59	140.92
Promethium	Pm	61	*147
Protactinium	Pa	91	231
Radium	Ra	88	226.05
Radon	Rn	86	222
Rhenium	Re	75	186.22
Rhodium	Rh	45	102.91
Rubidium	Rb	37	85.48
Ruthenium	Ru	44	101.1
Samarium	Sm	62	150.35
Scandium	Sc	21	44.96
Selenium	Se	34	78.96
Silicon	Si	14	28.09
Silver	Ag	47	107.880
Sodium	Na	11	22.991
Strontium	Sr	38	87.63
Sulfur	S	16	32.006
Tantalum	Ta	73	180.95
Technetium	Tc	43	*99
Tellurium	Te	52	127.61
Terbium	Tb	65	158.93
Thallium	Tl	81	204.39
Thorium	Th	90	232.05
Thulium	Tm	69	168.94
Tin	Sn	50	118.70
Titanium	Ti	22	47.90

† formerly Columbium

ABOUT THE AUTHOR

JUDITH VIORST is a staff writer for Science Service. Among the many assignments that she has completed for them are two books, *Projects: Space,* and *Wonderful World of Science,* with Shirley Moore. Science Service, Inc., is the non-profit Institution for the Popularization of Science. Its many ambitious projects include the famous science fairs held throughout the country, the National Science Fair-International, and the Science Talent Search. Another service is the publication of the SCIENCE NEWS LETTER which enables students and the general public to keep up with the latest information on developments in science.

Bantam Modern Classics

Available wherever paperbacks are sold

- -

UNIFACT BOOKS

A REVOLUTIONARY NEW WAY OF LEARNING!

Here is an exciting new programmed teaching method, now available in book form for the first time! The UNIFACT method is the easiest, most effective way yet devised for learning. Facts are presented one at a time, then the fact is fixed in memory through the immediate use of examples and quizzes. This step-by-step course of self-instruction teaches each subject easily and effectively. Students will find UNIFACT texts are aids to higher grades.

These four titles, chosen because of subject popularity, will be of major interest to high school and college students—especially chemistry and physics majors—their parents, teachers and general readers interested in forms and uses of science and mathematics.

SIMPLIFYING THE SLIDE RULE by Robert W. Marks. Introduced previously to great success, this book using the UNIFACT method makes all basic slide rule operations easy. One hour after beginning this book, anyone who has never seen a slide rule before, can use it efficiently. (SU1 • 75¢)

SIMPLIFYING ELECTRICITY by Bradley V. Smith. An elementary text explaining the nature, forms and basic applications of electricity and magnetism. Also discussed is the nature of the atom, calculations and circuits. (SU2 • 75¢)

SIMPLIFYING FRACTIONS AND DECIMALS by Bradley V. Smith. Using the key ideas of the "New Math," this basic text teaches clearly and simply all forms and meanings of fractions and decimals, explaining how to use them in all ordinary calculations. (SU3 • 75¢)

SIMPLIFYING SET THEORY by Robert W. Marks. Here is the most dynamic approach to mathematical logic, the heart of the "New Math" now being taught in all modern primary and high schools. The UNIFACT method of presentation makes learning this subject very easy. (SU4 • 75¢)

BANTAM SCIENCE AND MATHEMATICS

A provocative survey of the most up-to-date facts
and theories of modern science and mathematics

- ☐ THE ATOM & BEYOND: A New Introduction to Modern Physical Science, by E. Sheldon Smith. The principles and concepts of modern atomic science are clearly and concisely defined. (SA5/75¢)
- ☐ THE SEARCH FOR LIFE ON OTHER WORLDS. A fascinating up-to-the-minute and easy to understand story of the technology of space travel. (SA2/75¢)
- ☐ PROFILES OF THE FUTURE, by Arthur C. Clarke. New advances in the use of heredity, power, energy and space. (SA12/75¢)
- ☐ THE CHANGING EARTH. An illustrated study of modern geology. (SA2/75¢)
- ☐ WEATHER. Complete with photographs and drawings, here is everything you need to know about the world of weather. (HA1/60¢)
- ☐ RATS, LICE & HISTORY, by Hans Zinsser. The provocative biography of infectious diseases and the roles they have played in the history of man. (NA7/95¢)
- ☐ GREAT IDEAS IN MODERN SCIENCE. An excellent survey of the foundations of modern science with biographical and prefatory notes. (NA8/95¢)
- ☐ ONE, TWO, THREE . . . INFINITY, by George Gamow. A popular introduction to the facts and theories of modern science. (NA9/95¢)
- ☐ 150 SCIENCE EXPERIMENTS STEP-BY-STEP. Fascinating demonstrations of the basic principles of chemistry, biology, physics, weather and numbers. (HA10/60¢)
- ☐ MATHEMATICS TABLES & HOW TO USE THEM. A handbook of all mathematics tables and reference formulas needed for everyday work in school, laboratory and workshop. (SA6/75¢)
- ☐ THE NEW MATHEMATICS DICTIONARY & HANDBOOK. Comprehensively answers every kind of question about math in simple, clear nontechnical language. (NA7/95¢)
- ☐ THE NEW PHYSICS & CHEMISTRY DICTIONARY & HANDBOOK. A comprehensive and practical shop and laboratory reference book. (NA11/95¢)